GOODS OF THE MIND, LLC

Math Challenges

for

Gifted Students

PRACTICE TESTS IN

MATH KANGAROO STYLE

FOR STUDENTS IN GRADES 5-6

Cleo Borac, M. Sc.
Silviu Borac, Ph. D.

This edition published in 2017 in the United States of America.

Editing and proofreading: David Borac, M. Mus.
Technical support: Andrei T. Borac, B.A., PBK

Send all inquiries to:

Goods of the Mind, LLC
1138 Grand Teton Dr.
Pacifica
CA, 94044

Math Challenges for Gifted Students
Level III (Grades 5 and 6)
Practice Tests in Math Kangaroo Style for Students in Grades 5-6

Contents

FOREWORD

This workbook contains six exams that are similar to the Math Kangaroo contest, an international mathematics competition for students in grades 1 through 12. The contents of this book are not associated with the Math Kangaroo organization in any way. None of the problems included has been an actual contest problem. Also, problems are not repeated across the various books in our series. Each workbook presents a completely different set of original problems.

The problems in this book are somewhat more difficult than the ones of the actual competition. This is training material - therefore, the problems have been built so as to reflect the variety of concepts needed to prepare for this competition, rather than imitate exactly the format and difficulty level. In the authors' experience, training material should add more instructional value than practice based on past exam papers. For instance, easy problems provide opportunities for assessment but are low in instructional value, i.e. we do not learn much from them. For this reason, you will find our problems slightly more difficult. On the other hand, they are very helpful as training material, at least in the authors' experience.

The mathematical pre-requisites include only: addition and subtraction with multidigit numbers, multiplication of multi-digit numbers, integer division with remainder, ratios, operations with fractions, percents, rates, and recognition of the basic geometric figures and solids.

As in any contest paper, the difficulty of the items is staggered. The 3-point problems are relatively easy problems based on observation, elementary counting, and reading comprehension. The 4-point and the 5-point problems require more creative applications of the concepts studied in school at the specific grade level.

The authors recommend this book as an additional study material to the series "Competitive Mathematics for Gifted Students" - level 3. As the student progresses through the material of the series, these tests are useful for assessment as well as for training specific competitive skills such as: time management, stamina, and focusing over a longer period of time. We recommend taking one of these tests every month or so. The student should have 90 minutes of contiguous time to solve *without using a calculator*. Using scratch paper is strongly suggested. The student should make diagrams, tables, and show work for each problem.

TEST NUMBER ONE

3-point problems

✓ 1. In Kangarob's game, coloring a green square is worth 2 points and coloring an orange square is worth 1 point. How many points can he receive by coloring this figure?

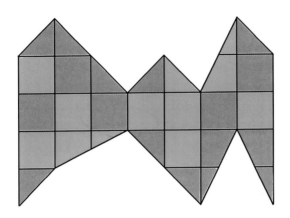

$2 + 2 + 2 + 2 + 2 + 2 + 2 + 2$
$+ 2 + 0.5 + 1 + 1 + 1 + 1 + 1 + 1 + 1$
$+ 1 + 1 + 1 + 1 + 1 + 1$

(A) 25.5 (B) 30 (C) 32 (D) 34 (E) 41

2. Elaine has 7 quarters (25 cent coins) and her brother Dan has some dimes (10 cent coins) and nickels (5 cent coins). What is the least number of coins Dan must have for them to have $2.50 in total?

(A) 5 (B) 6 (C) 7 (D) 8 (E) 9

$7 \times 0.25 = 1.75$ 2.25
1.85 2.35
1.95 2.45
2.05 2.50
2.15

3. Theo has figured out the missing number in the following number puzzle:

5	95
30	70
12	
15	85
75	25

What is the sum of the digits of that number?

(A) 9 (B) 10 (C) 12 (D) 14 (E) 16

4. Sandra has 5 friends. Sandra invites her friends. Each friend brings two friends of their own. What is the smallest possible number of people at Sandra's party?

(A) 5 (B) 6 (C) 8 (D) 15 (E) 16

5. The *semi-difference* of two integers is the half of their positive difference. For example, the semi-difference of 11 and 5 is $(11 - 5)/2 = 3$. If the semi-difference of two integers is an integer then the sum of the two integers is:

(A) always odd
(B) always even
(C) sometimes odd
(D) always a multiple of 4
(E) always a multiple of 8

6. Which number may be on the last leaf?

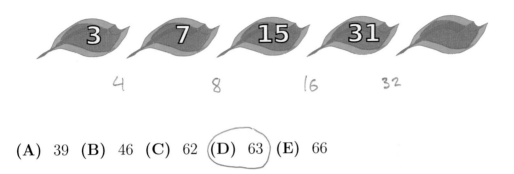

4 8 16 32

(A) 39 (B) 46 (C) 62 (D) 63 (E) 66

7. Which number is the largest multiple of 3 that is smaller than a multiple of 5 which is smaller than 40?

(A) 33 (B) 36 (C) 39 (D) 42 (E) 45

8. Which of the following operations produces an answer that is a multiple of 3?

 (A) $101 \times 103 \times 105$
 (B) $101 \times 103 \times 104$
 (C) $100 \times 101 \times 103$
 (D) $100 \times 103 \times 104$
 (E) $104 \times 106 \times 107$

9. A number exceeds 12 by twice as much as it exceeds 18. What is the number?

(A) 14 (B) 16 (C) 18 (D) 20 (E) 24

10. Which is the largest fraction?

(A) $\dfrac{22}{33}$

(B) $\dfrac{202}{303}$

(C) $\dfrac{2002}{3003}$

(D) $\dfrac{20002}{30003}$

(E) they are all equivalent

4-point problems

11. At least how many small squares must be moved in order to make the figure symmetric with respect to the line AB?

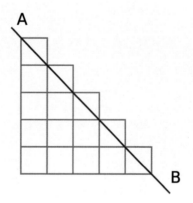

(A) 3 (B) 4 (C) 5 (D) 6 (E) 7

12. In Kangaroy's game, fields that are equally far from the center must be filled with numbers that are equidistant from 70. For example, 1 is 69 units far from 70 and so is 139. Moreover, the numbers must be in strictly increasing order from left to right. What is the largest number Kangaroy can place in the marked field?

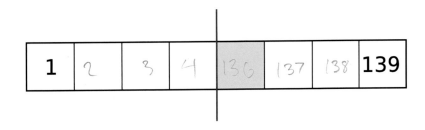

(A) 64 (B) 66 (C) 70 (D) 136 (E) 139

13. Three kangaroos race each other on a meadow. When the winner crosses the finish line, the second is one fifth of the race distance behind him, while the third one is one third of the race distance behind the first. As the winner crosses the finish line, the distance between the second and the third is what fraction of the total distance?

(A) $\dfrac{-2}{5}$ (B) $\dfrac{1}{15}$ (C) $\dfrac{1}{5}$ (D) $\dfrac{2}{15}$ (E) $\dfrac{3}{5}$

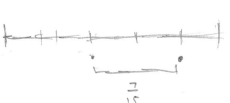

14. How many digits does the number N have?

$$N = 2 \times 2 \times 2 \times 2 \times 2 \times 5 \times 5 \times 5 \times 5 \times 5$$

(A) 2 (B) 3 (C) 4 (D) 5 (E) 6

60   50   40

50   40   30

40   30   20

30   20   10

R   Y   G

15. Sandra has three bags with apples. If she would move 10 apples from the red bag into the green bag, then all bags would have an equal number of apples. If she would move 10 apples from the green bag into the yellow bag, then there would be twice as many apples in the yellow bag as in the green bag. How many apples are there in the red bag?

(A) 20 (B) 30 (C) 40 (D) 50 (E) 60

16. Andy and Tessa start walking towards each other at the same time. By taking 2 steps, Andy covers the same distance as Tessa covers by taking 3 steps. They meet when each has taken 30 steps, 2 minutes after starting. How long would it take Tessa to walk the entire distance?

(A) 3.5 min

(B) 4 min

(C) 4.5 min

(D) 5 min

(E) 6 min

17. Two consecutive positive integers have a product of:

$$2 \times 3 \times 5 \times 19 \times 23$$

Which is their sum?

(A) 52 (B) 56 (C) 78 (D) 208 (E) 229

18. The water level indicator of a kettle looked like in the figure before and after 40% of its total water capacity was consumed. What is the capacity of the kettle, in cups?

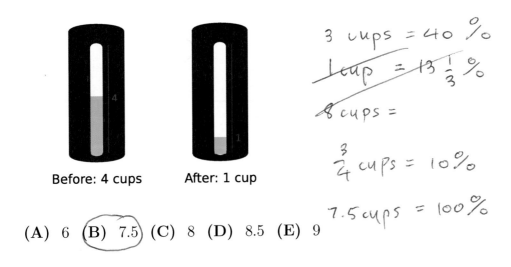

Before: 4 cups   After: 1 cup

3 cups = 40 %

1 cup = 13 $\frac{1}{3}$ %

8 cups =

$\frac{3}{4}$ cups = 10 %

7.5 cups = 100 %

(A) 6   (B) 7.5   (C) 8   (D) 8.5   (E) 9

19. The figure represents a diagram of flights planned within a Mars colony. The cubes represent buildings and each segment represents one connecting flight. At least how many connecting flights must be canceled so that there is only one possible way to travel from any building to any building?

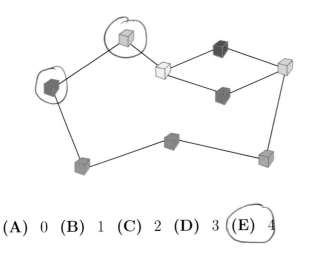

(A) 0   (B) 1   (C) 2   (D) 3   (E) 4

20. At a camp, a group of 22 students in grades 5 and 6 played a board game that requires 2 players. One 5th grader played the game with one 6th grader. Another 5th grader played this game with two 6th graders. Another 5th grader played this game with three 6th graders. This pattern continued until the last 5th grader played this game with all the 6th graders. How many games did the last 5th grader play?

(A) 10 (B) 11 (C) 13 (D) 15 (E) 17

5-point problems

21. A *unit fraction* is a fraction with numerator equal to 1, such as 1/5. If we subtract a unit fraction from its own denominator the resulting fraction is:

(A) always irreducible (in its simplest form)

(B) sometimes reducible by 2

(C) sometimes reducible by 3

(D) sometimes reducible by 5

(E) always reducible by the number at the denominator

$5 - \frac{1}{5} = 4\frac{4}{5}$

$10 - \frac{1}{10} = 9\frac{9}{10}$

$13 - \frac{1}{13} = 12\frac{1}{13}$

22. Jim said:
'Ben has twice as many cookies as Anna.'
Jill said:
'Anna has 3 cookies less than Jim.'
Ben said:
'Jill has 2 cookies more than Anna.'
The total number of cookies they have could be:

(A) 9 (B) 16 (C) 25 (D) 36 (E) 43

$B = 2A$

$A = J - 3$

$J = A + 2$

$J = (J - 3) + 2$

23. Which of the answer choices does NOT represent an expression equivalent to the following:

$$E = \frac{\frac{5}{6}}{\frac{7}{11}}$$

(A) $5 \times 11 \div 6 \div 7$ (B) $5 \div 6 \div 7 \times 11$ (C) $11 \div 7 \times 5 \div 6$

(D) $5 \div 6 \div 7 \div 11$ (E) $5 \div 7 \times 11 \div 6$

24. If A, B, and C are distinct digits and the following multiplication is correct:

A B A x A B A = A B C B A

then what is the sum $A + B + C$?

(A) 1 (B) 2 (C) 3 (D) 4 (E) 5

25. A rectangle with side lengths of 4 and 5 units, respectively, is completely cut into identical tiles of rectangular shape. If at least one cut must be made, how many possible sizes are there for the tiles? (Recall that squares are rectangles.)

(A) 3 (B) 4 (C) 5 (D) 6 (E) 7

26. Leah, Alma, and Thea are camping in the mountains. Every day, each of them writes a message to her parents. One day, they decide to do things differently and let each of them write to the parents of another. In how many different ways could they do this?

(A) 1 **(B)** 2 **(C)** 3 **(D)** 4 **(E)** 6

27. A rectangular shaped eraser with dimensions $3 \times 4 \times 5$ is dunked in paint and set on a sheet of paper. Then, the eraser is rotated clockwise around one of its sides that touch the paper. This operation is repeated 5 times. What is the length of the longest possible rectangular trace of paint on the paper?

(A) 21 **(B)** 23 **(C)** 27 **(D)** 40 **(E)** 60

28. How many (unordered) pairs of fractions from the set

$$\frac{1}{8}, \frac{1}{4}, \frac{3}{8}, \frac{1}{2}, \frac{5}{8}, \frac{3}{4}$$

do not have a sum of $\frac{7}{8}$? $\quad \frac{2}{8} \quad \frac{4}{8} \quad \frac{6}{8}$

(A) 3 **(B)** 8 **(C)** 10 **(D)** 12 **(E)** 15

29. Four distinct positive integers have a least common multiple of 210. However, any two of these numbers have a greatest common factor of 7. What is the sum of the four numbers?

(A) 30 **(B)** 37 **(C)** 42 **(D)** 70 **(E)** 77

30. A circular hole of area 12 square units has been cut out of a square of area 49 square units. The remaining shape has been cut into 4 congruent parts so that the bolded segment has length 3 units. The parts have been reassembled as a rectangle with a hole. What is the area of the hole in the rectangle (the shaded part of the figure), in square units?

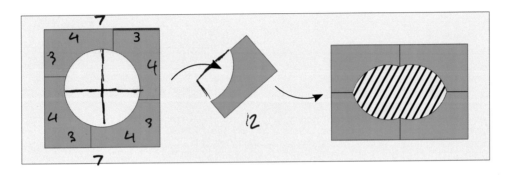

(A) 8 (B) 9 (C) 11 (D) 12 (E) 13

Answer Key for Test One

3-point problems	4-point problems	5-point problems
1. B	11. C	21. A
2. D	12. D	22. C
3. E	13. D	23. D
4. B	14. E	24. C
5. B	15. E	25. C
6. D	16. D	26. B
7. A	17. E	27. B
8. A	18. B	28. D
9. E	19. C	29. E
10. E	20. B	30. C

TEST NUMBER TWO

3-point problems

1. Joel and Tina live beside a lagoon. In the figure, the lagoon is colored in blue and the land is brown. How many bridges must Joel and Tina build over water in order to make a path that is shortest from Joel's house to Tina's house?

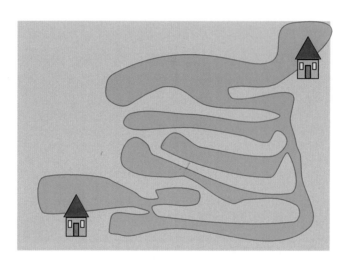

(A) 2 (B) 3 (C) 4 (D) 5 (E) 6

$2 + 4 + 3 + 1$

2. Jim is part of a reading club that has a reading contest happening over the summer. This past summer, 2 members of the club read the same number of books and they tied for first place in the contest. 4 members were ahead of Jim and 3 behind Jim. How many members does the club have?

(A) 7 (B) 8 (C) 9 (D) 10 (E) 11

3. A positive number differs from 12 by as much as 123 differs from 98. What is the sum of the digits of this number?

(A) 9 (B) 10 (C) 12 (D) 25 (E) 37

4. Two numbers are opposites of one another. Another two numbers are also opposites. Tom multiplies the negative numbers in the set of four numbers and Sandy multiplies the positive numbers. Tom's number:

(A) is equal to Sandy's number.
(B) is the opposite of Sandy's number.
(C) is smaller than Sandy's number.
(D) is larger than Sandy's number.
(E) is consecutive to Sandy's number.

5. Which of the figures labeled A, B, C, D, E, is NOT a rotation of the figure at the top?

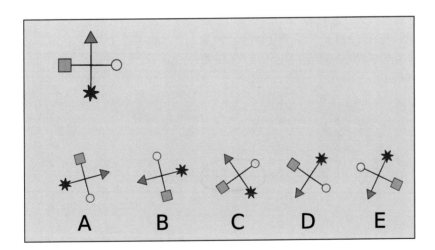

(A) A (B) B (C) C (D) D (E) E

2 : 35 ⎫
3 : 05 ⎬
3 : 35 ⎬
4 : 05 ⎬
4 : 35 ⎬
5 : 05 ⎭

6. Larry and Ron would like to play a game together. Each game is exactly 30 minutes long. Larry is free from 2:30 PM to 5:10 PM, while Ron is free from 2:35 PM to 5:20 PM. At most how many rounds of game can they play?

(A) 1 (B) 2 (C) 3 (D) 5 (E) 8

7. A bug moves along the side of a window. Each even minute it moves 5 inches forward and each odd minute is moves 2 inches backward. It starts at the bottom of the window at 10:00 AM. What time will it be when it reaches the top of the window, which is 23 inches higher?

(A) 10:10 AM (B) 10:11 AM (C) 10:12 AM
(D) 10:13 AM (E) 10:23 AM

8. Which operation does not have an answer that ends in zero?

(A) $2 \times 3 \times 5 \times 7$ (B) 4×35 (C) 15×18
(D) 38×45 (E) 54×52

9. Each member of the Readkins family starts reading a new book as soon as they finished reading the current one, but they do not read on vacation. It takes John 2 days to finish a book, Alexa takes 4 days to read a book, and Tanya takes 5 days for each book she reads. After coming back from vacation, how many days does it take them to read a total of 38 different books?

(A) 10 (B) 20 (C) 30 (D) 40 (E) 50

10. How many of the multiples of 3 in the following list of numbers are also multiples of 9?

$$69, 96, 312, 405, 522, 339, 1008, 2001, 777, 333$$

(A) 3 (B) 4 (C) 5 (D) 6 (E) 7

4-point problems

11. In the isometric grid, cube assemblies are specified by the number of cubes that form a vertical column in the assembly. For example,

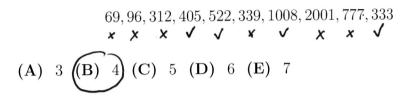

Which of the specifications A-E corresponds to the assembly on the left?

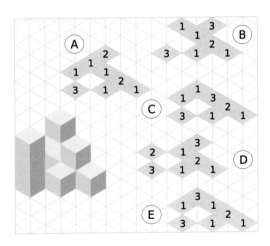

(A) A (B) B (C) C (D) D (E) E

12. Five friends, three girls and two boys, enter the House of Horrors one at a time. If the girls want to follow each other, how many ways are there for the five friends to enter the attraction?

(A) 6 (B) 12 (C) 18 (D) 36 (E) 120

13. By how much percent is the area of the hexagon larger than the area of the triangle?

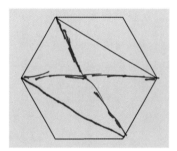

(A) 200% (B) 300% (C) 400% (D) 500% (E) 600%

14. Chris, Dan, and Emily take chips out of a bag. Chris takes 5, Dan takes 9, and Emily takes 12. Then Chris takes 17, and so on. They keep taking turns to remove chips according to the sequence:

$$5, 9, 13, 17, \ldots$$

At some point, they stop. Which one of them will take 57 chips at a time?

(A) Chris
(B) Dan
(C) Emily
(D) None of them
(E) Impossible to determine

15. The binary operator ∇ has the following behavior:

$$7\nabla 3 = \frac{7-3}{7+3} = \frac{4}{10} = \frac{2}{5}$$

Which of the following operations does NOT equal $\frac{3}{7}$?

(A) $5\nabla 2$ (B) $15\nabla 6$ (C) $10\nabla 4$
(D) $25\nabla 10$ (E) $20\nabla 6$

16. Among the numbers from 121 and 256 how many multiples of 3 end with the digit 7?

(A) 3 (B) 4 (C) 5 (D) 9 (E) 45

17. Each of four students contribute the same amount of money each to a wildlife organization. If six more students join this action, each would have to contribute a lower amount if they wanted to send the same total amount. The new individual contribution would be less than the initial one by how much percent?

(A) 40% (B) 50% (C) 60% (D) 70% (E) 75%

18. How many prime factors does 4321 have?

(A) 1 (B) 2 (C) 3 (D) 4 (E) 5

19. At most how many intersections can four lines have, if no two of them are parallel?

(A) 4 (B) 5 (C) 6 (D) 7 (E) 8

20. The double of the number 0.9999..., where the digit 9 repeats indefinitely is:

(A) 1.888... (B) 1.988... (C) 1.899... (D) 1.998... (E) 2

5-point problems

21. What is the smallest possible positive difference between a multiple of 64 and a multiple of 16?

(A) 2 (B) 4 (C) 8 (D) 16 (E) 64

22. In the scalene triangle $\triangle ABC$ there are angles with measures as marked in the figure. What is the measure of the angle x, in degrees of arc?

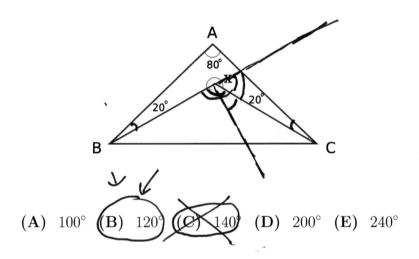

(A) 100° (B) 120° (C) 140° (D) 200° (E) 240°

23. A bag contains marbles of identical shape but different colors: red, blue, and green. Tony removes some green marbles and replaces them with red and blue marbles so that there are equal numbers of marbles of each color in the bag. Which of the following could be the number of marbles in the bag?

(A) 19 (B) 20 (C) 21 (D) 22 (E) 23

24. Three numbers are having a conversation. The first number says:
'I can be a remainder from a division by 8 but surely not a remainder from a division by 4.'

The second number says:
'I can be a remainder from a division by 6 but surely not a remainder from a division by 3.'

The third number says:
'I am smaller than one of you and larger than the other.'

What is the number of possible values there can be for the third number that spoke?

(A) 0 (B) 1 (C) 2 (D) 3 (E) 4

25. Farmer Stan has some chickens and dogs. The ratio of chickens to dogs is 51 : 2. After one third of the chickens were sold, the ratio of chicken legs to dog legs was:

(A) 17 : 2 (B) 17 : 4 (C) 34 : 1 (D) 17 : 1 (E) 17 : 8

26. Which of the rectangles A through E is the reflection of rectangle ABCD across from point Q?

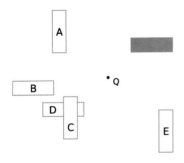

(A) A (B) B (C) C (D) D (E) E

27. A chicken weighs 5 lbs, a duck weighs 8 lbs, a goose weighs 11 lbs, and a turkey weighs 19 lbs. Farmer Stan went to the market with equal numbers of each kind of fowl. He made his first sale of a bird and then the remaining birds weighed 465 lbs in total. What kind of bird did he sell?

(A) chicken (B) duck (C) goose

(D) turkey (E) cannot be determined

28. A clock displays the time in 24-hour notation. For example, 23 : 15 is the same as 11 : 15 PM. How many times during a whole day does the clock display a time that has multiples of 11 in both the hours and the minutes places?

(A) 5 (B) 6 (C) 7 (D) 10 (E) 18

29. A 3-digit number has even digits. The ones digit is equal to the sum of the other 2 digits. How many such numbers are there?

(A) 10 (B) 20 (C) 40 (D) 60 (E) 100

30. Which of the following numbers is NOT a multiple of 13?

(A) 1231653423 (B) 4815152342 (C) 3713959249 (D) 8518902392
(E) 2152831333

Answer Key for Test Two

3-point problems	4-point problems	5-point problems
1. D	11. A	21. D
2. B	12. D	22. E
3. B	13. D	23. C
4. A	14. B	24. D
5. D	15. E	25. A
6. D	16. B	26. D
7. D	17. C	27. B
8. E	18. B	28. E
9. D	19. C	29. A
10. B	20. E	30. E

Test Number Three

3-point problems

1. Yesterday, the sun set at 8:15 PM and today, it rose at 6:35 AM. How long was the night?

   (A) 9 hrs and 20 minutes

   (B) 10 hrs and 20 minutes

   (C) 10 hrs and 40 minutes

   (D) 11 hrs and 20 minutes

   (E) 11 hrs and 40 minutes

2. One hundred one hundred dollar bills total:

   (A) $1,000

   (B) $10,000

   (C) $100,000

   (D) $1,000,000

   (E) $10,000,000

3. Which kangaroo made the highest jump?

   (A) Jim jumped 2,700 mm

   (B) Ben jumped 40 dm

   (C) Sam jumped 2.5 m

   (D) Jon jumped 300 cm

   (E) Ali jumped 0.005 km

4. Which of the following operations has an odd result?

(A) (odd+odd+odd)×(odd+odd)

(B) (odd+odd)-(odd+odd)

(C) (odd×odd+odd)×odd

(D) odd×odd×odd-odd

(E) odd-odd+odd-odd+odd

5. The figure represents a grid painted in checkerboard manner:

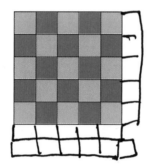

How many of the following operations will produce a grid that has the same number of small squares of each color?

- Add one more row following the same pattern.

- Add one more column following the same pattern.

- Add one more row and then one more column following the same pattern.

- Add one more row, then one more column, then one more row, following the same pattern.

- Add one more row, then one more column, then one more row, and then one more column following the same pattern.

(A) 1 (B) 2 (C) 3 (D) 4 (E) 5

6. Tony has 57 cars on the lot. He has to put winter tires on one third of them. How many winter tires does he have to install?

(A) 19 (B) 38 (C) 76 (D) 152 (E) 228

7. $8 \times 0.125 \times 2 \times 0.5 \times 4 \times 0.25$ equals:

(A) 0.5 (B) 0.75 (C) 1 (D) 1.2 (E) 1.5

8. A rectangle is not a square and has a perimeter of 8 units. If its side lengths are whole numbers, what is its area, in square units?

(A) 2 (B) 3 (C) 7 (D) 8 (E) 15

9. Three different positive integers are used to make fractions that are different from 1. At most how many of these fractions are larger than 1?

(A) 0 (B) 1 (C) 2 (D) 3 (E) 4

10. Which operation does not have the same result as the others?

(A) $\dfrac{4+5}{\frac{1}{4}+\frac{1}{5}}$ (B) $\dfrac{1}{\frac{1}{4}-\frac{1}{5}}$ (C) 4×5 (D) $4+5$ (E) $4 \times 4 + 4$

4-point problems

11. What is the greatest common factor of the numbers 1938 and 1734?

(A) 2 (B) 6 (C) 34 (D) 51 (E) 102

12. Hannah has a blank paper square without any markings. She wants to fold it so that the four vertices meet at the center, forming exactly a smaller square, like in the figure:

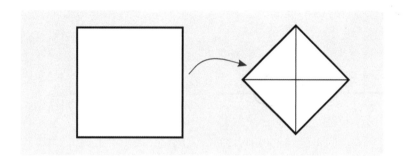

At least how many times does Hannah need to crease the original square in order to obtain an exactly square result?

(A) 2 (B) 4 (C) 6 (D) 8 (E) 10

13. Which of the following operations has the largest answer?

(A) $\dfrac{1}{3} + \dfrac{1}{7}$ (B) $\dfrac{1}{3+7}$ (C) $\dfrac{1}{3} \div \dfrac{1}{7}$

(D) $\dfrac{1}{\frac{1}{3} + \frac{1}{7}}$ (E) $\dfrac{1}{7} \div \dfrac{1}{3}$

14. Kangarob purchased 12 dozen eggs and Kangaroy purchased 7 dozen eggs. Since Kangarob did not have enough money, Kangaroy paid 50 dollars. Later on, Kangarob gave Kangaroy 15 dollars to settle his debt. How much money did Kangarob have initially?

(A) 30 (B) 35 (C) 40 (D) 45 (E) 50

15. An equilateral triangle is inscribed in a circle which is inscribed in a square such that one of the sides of the triangle is parallel to one of the sides of the square:

An operation consists of a clockwise rotation of the figure by 45° . Which of the following figures cannot be obtained by repeating this operation a number of times?

(A) A **(B)** B **(C)** C **(D)** D **(E)** E

16. The numbers from 0 to 99 inclusive are placed in boxes according to the sum of their digits. For example, 33 and 51 are in the same box because they both have the sum of the digits equal to 6. How many of the boxes have exactly 4 numbers inside?

(A) 0 **(B)** 2 **(C)** 8 **(D)** 9 **(E)** 10

17. Alex wrote a number on the whiteboard. Dan wrote the same number after Alex's number, without any spaces. Then, Samuel exclaimed: 'The new number is exactly 10001 times as large as the one Alex wrote!'
How many digits does the number written by Alex have?

(A) 2 **(B)** 3 **(C)** 4 **(D)** 5 **(E)** 6

18. Two opposite faces of a cube are selected and the other faces are discarded. One of the two selected faces is rotated 45°, like in the figure:

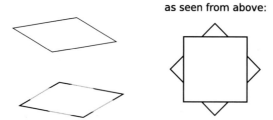

as seen from above:

At least how many additional planar faces must be used in order to form a convex polyhedron?

(Planar means the face is a part of a plane surface. A polyhedron is a solid with polygonal faces. Convex means that any two points on the surface of the solid can be connected by a segment that does not have points outside of the polyhedron.)

(A) 4 **(B)** 5 **(C)** 6 **(D)** 7 **(E)** 8

19. Robot A makes 5 zogs per minute, while robot B makes 6 zogs per minute. Both robots start at the same time, but after a while robot B runs out of material. Robot C notices this and supplies robot B with material. One hour after starting, robots A and B have made the same number of zogs each. How many minutes was robot B unable to produce zogs?

(A) 2 **(B)** 5 **(C)** 10 **(D)** 20 **(E)** 60

20. A train travels at 65 mph towards another train traveling at 55 mph from the opposite direction, on a parallel line. When they are 1.2 miles apart, one of the trains turns a light on. For how many seconds is the light visible by the driver of the other train?

(A) 20 seconds **(B)** 30 seconds **(C)** 36 seconds
(D) 40 seconds **(E)** 45 seconds

5-point problems

21. The diagonal of a square with area 49 is extended so as to double its length. What is the shaded area?

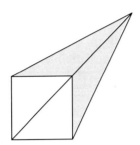

(A) 7 **(B)** 14 **(C)** 28 **(D)** 49 **(E)** 90

22. Aldo's hiking club counted the number of rainy days and found that it represented 30% of the total number of days they monitored. They also found that there were 20 more days without rain than with rain. How many days did their study last?

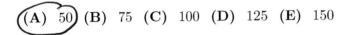

(A) 50 **(B)** 75 **(C)** 100 **(D)** 125 **(E)** 150

23. Esha had a whole number that she multiplied by 7. Then, she divided the result by 111 and obtained a whole number answer. What is the smallest number that this answer can be?

(A) 1 **(B)** 3 **(C)** 7 **(D)** 9 **(E)** 37

24. A container is filled with oil. An operation consists of consuming one fifth of the oil present in the container. After the operation has been performed three times, 61 gallons of oil have been consumed in total. How many gallons of oil have remained in the container?

(A) 36 **(B)** 48.8 **(C)** 39.04 **(D)** 64 **(E)** 183

25. Alissa has 2 sticks of length 1, 2 sticks of length 2, and 1 stick of length 3. How many different triangles can she make if she is allowed to reuse the sticks?

(A) 5 (B) 6 (C) 8 (D) 10 (E) 25

26. Emily wrote the number 20009. Then, she subtracted from it the sum of its digits. Then, she added to the result the sum of *its* digits. Then, she subtracted from the result the sum of *its* digits. Having nothing better to do, Emily continued in this pattern for a while. What number did she have after the 1000th operation?

(A) 19998 (B) 20034 (C) 20025 (D) −20009 (E) cannot be determined

27. At TallTree Farms, Jim supervised the bagging of one fourth of the potato crop, Jack supervised the bagging of half the amount Jim did, Jared continued on the next shift and bagged another third as much as Jack, while John bagged the rest. How many times larger was John's portion than Jared's?

(A) 13 (B) 14 (C) 15 (D) 16 (E) 24

28. Chris, Dan, and Emily take chips out of a bag. Chris takes 3, Dan takes 6, and Emily takes 9. Then Chris takes 12, and so on. They keep taking turns to remove chips according to the sequence:

$$3, 6, 9, 12, \ldots$$

As Chris has taken out a total of 66 chips, what is the total number of chips Emily has taken out?

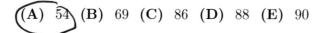 (A) 54 (B) 69 (C) 86 (D) 88 (E) 90

29. In five identical squares of side 8 units, some areas have been painted darker. How many of the figures have the same darker area?

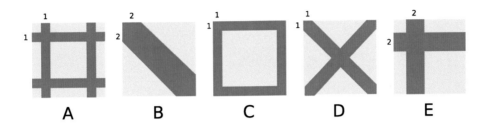

A   B   C   D   E

(A) 2 **(B)** 3 **(C)** 4 **(D)** 5 **(E)** they are all different

30. Which of the numbers is a perfect square? (A *perfect square* is a whole number that is the product of a whole number with itself. For example, some perfect squares are the bolded ones in the following sequence: $\mathbf{1} = 1 \times 1. \mathbf{4} = 2 \times 2, \mathbf{9} = 3 \times 3, \ldots$, etc.)

(A) 5508402 **(B)** 5508403 **(C)** 5508407
(D) 5508408 **(E)** 5508409

Answer Key for Test Three

3-point problems	4-point problems	5-point problems
1. B	11. E	21. D
2. B	12. C	22. A
3. E	13. C	23. C
4. E	14. D	24. D
5. D	15. A	25. C
6. C	16. B	26. B
7. C	17. C	27. B
8. B	18. E	28. A
9. D	19. C	29. D
10. D	20. C	30. E

TEST NUMBER FOUR

3-point problems

1. Wanda's birthday cake weighs three-fifths of a pound more than three-fifths of the cake. How many pounds does the whole cake weigh?

   (A) 1 **(B)** 1.5 **(C)** 2 **(D)** 2.5 **(E)** 5

2. Kangaroo K wakes up at 5:25 AM, kangaroo A wakes up 50 minutes later, kangaroo N wakes up 25 minutes before kangaroo A, kangaroo G wakes up at 6:05 AM, and kangaroo R wakes up later than N but earlier than G. Which of the following could be the time when kangaroo R wakes up?

   (A) $5:30$ AM **(B)** $5:35$ AM **(C)** $5:40$ AM
   (D) $5:45$ AM **(E)** $5:55$ AM

3. Laura has three blocks with the same width of 2 and the same height of 2 but different lengths of 2, 3, and 5 units. She wants to use one or more blocks at a time to build a tower assembly. How many different heights can an assembly have?

   (A) 5 **(B)** 6 **(C)** 7 **(D)** 8 **(E)** 9

4. A table consists of 9 different entries:

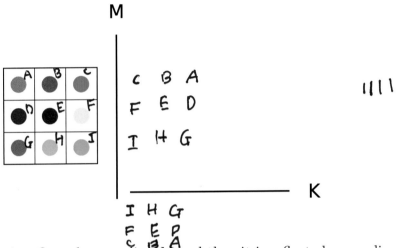

First, it is reflected across line M and then it is reflected across line K. How many of the entries have changed both their row and their column with respect to the original table?

(A) 0 (B) 2 (C) 4 (D) 6 (E) 8

5. Calculate:

$$900 - 850 + 800 - 750 + \cdots + 200 - 150 =$$

50 + 50 50

(A) 400 (B) 450 (C) 500 (D) 550 (E) 600

6. On Jupiter, each day is 10 hours long. If a probe photographed the surface of Jupiter at 5:15 and then again after 7 hours and 50 minutes, what time was the second photograph taken at?

(A) 7:50 (B) 12:65 (C) 13:05 (D) 2:05 (E) 3:05

7. Maxwell's Demon stands in the opening between two chambers and whacks the blue atoms into the same chamber and the yellow atoms into the same chamber, effectively separating the blue ones from the yellow ones. Assuming it whacks them with the same frequency, in which of the following five situations will the Demon take the shortest time to completely separate the two kinds of atoms?

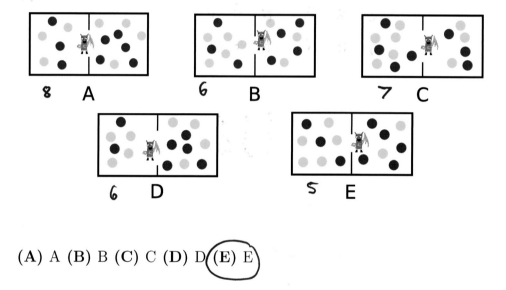

8 A   6 B   7 C

6 D   5 E

(A) A **(B)** B **(C)** C **(D)** D **(E)** E

8. Which of the numbers is not a multiple of 3?

(A) 333222111 **(B)** 333111222 **(C)** 122113233
(D) 311211223 **(E)** 323213121

9. On the hill, there are some white-tail deer. There are bucks, does, and juveniles. There are 3 more juveniles than other deer. There are 10 deer of one of the three kinds. At least how many deer are there on the hill?

(A) 17 **(B)** 20 **(C)** 21 **(D)** 25 **(E)** 27

10. How many squares with integer side lengths have areas between 121 and 441 inclusive?

(A) 10 (B) 11 (C) 12 (D) 160 (E) 320

4-point problems

11. Gina has 120 identical wooden blocks with width and height both equal to 8 and length of 2 units. How many cubical boxes with dimensions $16 \times 16 \times 16$ does she need to fit them all in?

(A) 2 (B) 4 (C) 5 (D) 6 (E) 8

12. 4% of a positive number equals the reciprocal of the number. Which of the following statements is true?

(A) The number is prime.
(B) The number is even.
(C) The number is smaller than 1.
(D) The number is not an integer.
(E) There are more than one such numbers.

13. Two hikers start climbing together on the Hazelnut Trail. At two thirds of the way up, one of them decided to camp and cook while the other continued to the top and returned 3 hours after they split. If walking is done always at the same speed, how many hours will it take them to return from the campsite to the start of the trail?

(A) 1.5 (B) 2 (C) 2.5 (D) 3 (E) 6

14. If $3m + 5n$ equals 150% of $6m$, then what percentage of m does n represent?

    (A) 80% **(B)** 90% **(C)** 120% **(D)** 150% **(E)** 180%

15. A right angle triangle has $AC = 8$ a right angle at point C. The vertex A moves downwards

    at a speed of 1 inch/min.

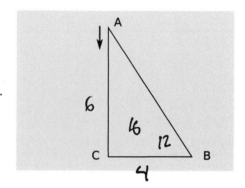

    After two minutes, the area of the triangle has decreased by:

    (A) 75% **(B)** 60% **(C)** 50% **(D)** 30% **(E)** 25%

16. Holly receives from her friends a bag of marbles of the same shape but different colors.

    - '11 marbles are not red,' says Yesenia.
    - 'There are 29 marbles in total,' says Carla.
    - '13 marbles are not blue,', says James.
    - '5 marbles are neither red nor blue,' says Pearl.
    - 'There are 19 marbles in total,' says Jorge.

    One of Holly's friends counted wrong, but the others are all correct. Which one counted wrong?

    (A) Yesenia **(B)** Carla **(C)** James **(D)** Pearl **(E)** Jorge

17. If the squares in the figure have side lengths $a, b, c,$ and d, which of the following represents the perimeter of the entire figure?

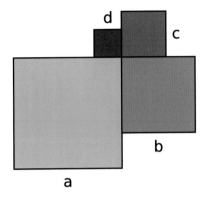

(A) $4(a+c)-2(b+d)$ (B) $4(a+b+c+d)$ (C) $4(a+c)+2(b+d)$
(D) $4a+2(b+c+d)$ (E) $4a+2b+2c$

18. Which of the following fractions is equivalent to a terminating decimal?

(A) $\dfrac{2}{300}$ (B) $\dfrac{2}{325}$ (C) $\dfrac{2}{425}$ (D) $\dfrac{2}{525}$ (E) $\dfrac{2}{625}$

19. How many numbers are there in the sequence?

$+6$

$$4, 10, 16, 22, \ldots, 202$$

(A) 32   (B) 33   (C) 34   (D) 35   (E) 36

20. Tom counts by 2s from 98 down to 0 and Jack counts by 5s from 0 to 245 at the same time. When Tom says '46' what number does Jack say?

(A) 120 (B) 125 (C) 130 (D) 135 (E) 140

5-point problems

21. A pirate has 11 silver coins and 20 gold coins. His friend asks him to play a game with the following rules: take 2 coins at random from the bag. If they are both gold, give them to the friend, if they are both silver the friend will replace them with gold coins, and if they are different, the friend will replace the silver one by a gold one. The pirate figures he stands to gain and plays the game for a while. After a while:

    (A) He has only one silver coin left.

    (B) He has only two gold coins left.

    (C) He has gained some more coins from his friend.

    (D) He has no coins left.

    (E) He has one gold coin and one silver coin left.

22. How many points are closer to points A and M than to points B and N (not including A, M, B, N)?

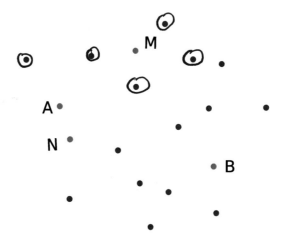

    (A) 1 **(B)** 2 **(C)** 3 **(D)** 4 **(E)** 5

23. Frank has been given a problem about a scalene trapezoid that has a perimeter of 10 units. All the side lengths are integer numbers. Frank does not know how to assign the side lengths to the sides. Can you help him?

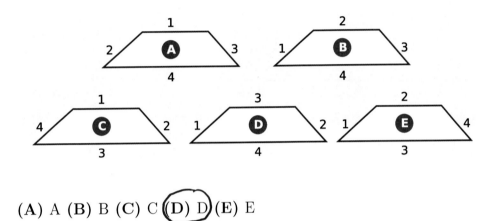

(A) A (B) B (C) C (D) D (E) E

24. Terry printed posters for the math contest at his school. He printed 20% of the posters on blue paper, 30% of the posters on yellow paper, and the rest on green paper. If he grabs 15 posters at random, he is sure to have at least one yellow poster among them. How many green posters are there?

(A) 10 (B) 12 (C) 14 (D) 15 (E) 30

25. Tanya had a coupon when she went shopping. However, the store also had a different promotion. Tanya figured out that, when applied to her purchase, the 30% off promotion was better by $1 than her $20 off coupon. Since only one of the reductions could be applied, Tanya chose the more advantageous one. How much did Tanya pay for her purchase in the end?

(A) 20 (B) 35 (C) 49 (D) 70 (E) cannot be determined

26. The digits A, B and C are different and the numbers AB and AC are 2-digit consecutive even numbers. The following operation is correct:

$$AB \times AC = CAB$$

Find the sum of the digits of the result: $A + B + C$.

(A) 10 **(B)** 12 **(C)** 14 **(D)** 16 **(E)** 17

27. An arrow points upwards. If we say it points to zero, then clockwise rotations are positive and counter-clockwise rotations are negative. For example:

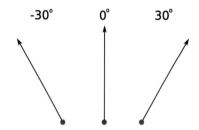

An operation consists of rotating the arrow clockwise by $30°$ if the operation has an even count, and counterclockwise by $90°$, if the operation has an odd count. For example, 3 operations will rotate the arrow by $-90° + 30° - 90° = -150°$. If the arrow points initially directly upwards, which of the choices represents the result of applying the operation 1200 times?

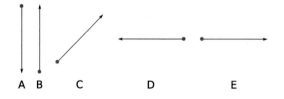

(A) A (B) B (C) C (D) D (E) E

28. Four friends play a board game that requires two partners. Each round takes 20 minutes and they only have 40 minutes to play. In how many different ways can they form teams so that each of them plays the whole time?

(A) 1 (B) 2 (C) 3 (D) 4 (E) 6

29. What is the value of

$$(2016^2 - 2015 \times 2017)^{2017}$$

(A) 1 (B) 2016^{2017} (C) 2015^{2016} (D) 2016^{4034} (E) 1013^{4034}

30. Tony biked one mile in 4 minutes and another mile 40% faster. What was his average speed, in miles per hour?

(A) 12.5 (B) 13 (C) 17.5 (D) 18 (E) 22.2

Answer Key for Test Four

3-point problems	4-point problems	5-point problems
1. B	11. B	21. A
2. E	12. A	22. C
3. E	13. D	23. A
4. C	14. C	24. A
5. A	15. E	25. C
6. E	16. B	26. B
7. E	17. E	27. B
8. D	18. E	28. C
9. A	19. C	29. A
10. B	20. C	30. C

TEST NUMBER FIVE

3-point problems

1. How many more minutes are there in one day than in one hour?

    (A) 11×60 **(B)** 12×60 **(C)** 23×60 **(D)** 24×60 **(E)** 99×60

2. How many 2-digit numbers have digits that differ by 7?

    (A) 2 **(B)** 4 **(C)** 5 **(D)** 14 **(E)** 49

3. There are 4 students in a group. The instructor draws a regular polygon with 64 sides. Each student comes and draws segments to connect the midpoints of each pair of neighboring sides, forming a new polygon. The next student performs the same operation with the new polygon, and so on, until each student has had a turn. At the end of the process, the polygon drawn by the last student is a polygon with

    (A) 4 sides **(B)** 8 sides **(C)** 16 sides **(D)** 32 sides **(E)** 64 sides

4. $7 \times 11 \times 13 \times 555 =$

    (A) 5550555 **(B)** 55055055 **(C)** 555555
    (D) 555000 **(E)** 505050

5. Which of the answer choices could be the next number in the sequence?

    $$3, 4, 7, 9, 11, 14, 15, 19, 19, 24, \ldots$$

    (A) 23 **(B)** 24 **(C)** 25 **(D)** 26 **(E)** 27

6. The assembly of equilateral triangles rotates clockwise around point P 60° at a time. Which of the A-E positions will the assembly be in after 100 rotations?

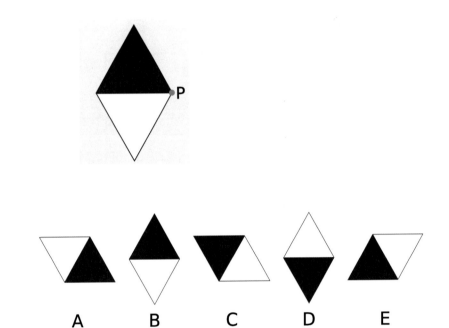

A   B   C   D   E

(A) A (B) B (C) C (D) D (E) E

7. How many of the following numbers are equal to their reciprocal?

$$-10, -1, -0.1, 0, 0.1, 1, 10$$

(A) none (B) 1 (C) 2 (D) 3 (E) 5

8. What is the length of the shortest path that a garbage truck can use in order to pick up the garbage on the streets in the figure? The truck can enter and leave from any street corner.

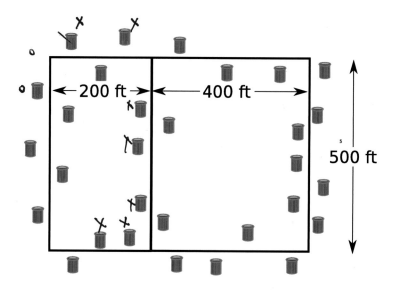

200 ft   400 ft   500 ft

(A) 2200 (B) 2700 (C) 2900 (D) 3100 (E) 3200

9. In a basket, 30% of the capacity (i.e. volume) is taken by some oranges and the rest is air. If we put 20 more oranges in the basket, 30% of the capacity is taken by air and the rest is oranges. How many oranges were there in the basket initially?

(A) 10 (B) 15 (C) 20 (D) 50 (E) 60

10. Which of the results of the following operations is largest?

78400   78 3 99   78 3 9 6

(A) 280×280 (B) 279×281 (C) 278×282

(D) 277×283 (E) 276×284

78391   78 384

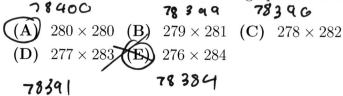

4-point problems

11. Two rectangles with a common side of length 4 have widths that add up to a length of 12. If the area shaded in grey is equal to 8 square units, what is the total dark blue area in square units?

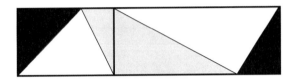

(A) 8 **(B)** 12 **(C)** 14 **(D)** 15 **(E)** 16

12. How many proper fractions with denominator 6 are larger than $\frac{1}{7}$ and smaller than $\frac{2}{3}$?

(A) 3 **(B)** 4 **(C)** 6 **(D)** 7 **(E)** an infinity

13. The product of the digits of an even 11-digit number is a prime number. Which of the following numbers is the number NOT divisible by?

(A) 2 **(B)** 3 **(C)** 4 **(D)** 8 **(E)** 16

14. Andy has some chickens. By day, the chickens roam in the field. At night, Andy must help them get in their coops. If Andy puts 3 chickens in each coop, there are 8 chickens left over. If he puts 4 chickens in each coop, there is one coop left empty. Andy decides to put 3 chickens in some of the coops and 4 chickens in the others. How many coops have 3 chickens in them?

(A) 2 **(B)** 3 **(C)** 4 **(D)** 5 **(E)** 6

15. What is the average of all the acute angles in the figure?

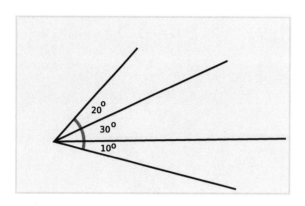

(A) 20° (B) 30° (C) 35° (D) 40° (E) 60°

16. What is the largest prime factor of the number:

$$1000^{1001} - 1000^{1000}$$

(A) 3 (B) 7 (C) 11 (D) 13 (E) 37

17. Which of the following may have a result that is not a multiple of 3?

(A) the sum of a number and twice its sum of digits
(B) the sum of the digits of the number with twice the number
(C) the difference of a number and its sum of digits
(D) the sum of a number and its sum of digits
(E) the sum of a number and eleven times its sum of digits

18. The four tiles rotate clockwise from the initial positions shown in the figure:

  tile NW rotates 90° per minute;

  tile NE rotates 180° per minute;

  tile SE rotates 270° per minute;

  tile SW rotates 360° per minute.

After 4 minutes all rotations stop and Tricia places the tiles in the large square. What is the sum of the numbers in the grey portion of the large square?

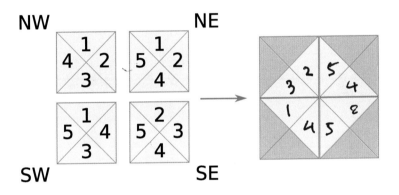

(A) 20 (B) 21 (C) 23 (D) 25 (E) 28

19. Each of ten children receive two cards of different color. No two children have the exact same pair of colors. Of at least how many different colors are the cards?

(A) 3 (B) 4 (C) 5 (D) 6 (E) 10

20. Two rectangles with side lengths 3 and 4 units are placed inside a circle like in the figure, without overlapping. The point O is the center of the circle. What is the area of the shaded rectangle? (The figure is not to scale.)

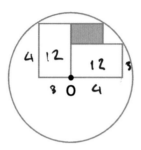

(A) 2 (B) 2.5 (C) 3 (D) 3.5 (E) 4

5-point problems

21. Alan wants to write the number 34 as a sum of 6 different positive integers (whole numbers). At least how many of them are odd?

(A) 0 (B) 1 (C) 2 (D) 4 (E) 6

22. A farmer has two harvesters. One harvester is newer and started harvesting at 6 AM. The other harvester needed some repairs and started harvesting at 1 PM. By 9 PM the entire field was harvested. If the older harvester would have started 2 hours earlier, the harvest would have ended at 8 PM. Which harvester harvests faster?

(A) The older harvester harvests faster.
(B) The newer harvester harvests faster.
(C) Both harvesters harvest at the same rate.
(D) It is not possible to find out from the data.
(E) It depends on the size of the field.

23. Anna and Tim start with the same number. Anna increases it by 1. Tim multiplies it by 2 and adds 7 to the result. Anna says 'Our numbers are not coprime.' Tim replies: 'Yes, they are both divisible by...'

 **(A)** 2 **(B)** 3 **(C)** 5 **(D)** 7 **(E)** 11

24. In a box, there are 20 yellow and orange tennis balls. 80% of them are yellow. Jamie adds balls to the box in the following pattern: 2 orange balls followed by 1 yellow ball. How many balls are there in the box by the time there are 60% yellow balls for the first time?

(A) 30 **(B)** 31 **(C)** 32 **(D)** 34 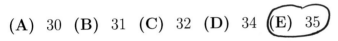 **(E)** 35

25. In a game of dominoes, there are 28 rectangular tiles. Each tile is subdivided into two squares and in each square there is a number of dots (*pips*) from 0 to 6, inclusive. All tiles are symmetrical: by rotating a tile, one simply swaps the two numbers, i.e. $(3,2)$ becomes $(2,3)$. Chain of dominoes can be made if the two adjacent sides of two dominoes have the same number of pips. Lisa makes a chain of dominoes so that the total number of pips on the chain is 5. What is the number of dominoes in the longest chain she can build?

(A) 3 **(B)** 4 **(C)** 5 **(D)** 6 **(E)** 7

26. The points of the grid are separated by 1 unit of length both in the vertical and the horizontal directions. By connecting any two points with a segment, how many different lengths are obtained?

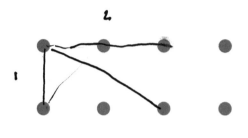

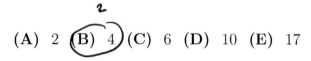

(A) 2 (B) 4 (C) 6 (D) 10 (E) 17

27. If a number's digits have a product that is smaller than their sum, we will call the number *florid*. How many 2-digit florid numbers are there?

(A) 25 (B) 26 (C) 27 (D) 28 (E) 30

28. Anna and Stella jump on a path made of tiles. Anna starts on the first tile and Stella starts on the fourth tile. Each second, they jump. Anna jumps over 3 tiles at a time and Stella jumps over 5 tiles. They stop after 1 minute has passed. How many tiles were stepped on by both of them?

(A) 0 (B) 30 (C) 31 (D) 60 (E) 120

29. On a fence there are some birds. On each of half of the planks there is at least one bird and on each of a third of the planks there are exactly two birds. There are 30 birds on the fence in total. At most, how many planks of the fence do not have any birds on them?

(A) 5 (B) 6 (C) 15 (D) 18 (E) 20

30. Jeremy climbs up any slope at 3 miles per hour and climbs down any slope at 5 miles per hour. A trail has a upslope that is twice as long as the downslope. If Jeremy starts at one end of the trail it takes him 40 minutes longer to reach the other end as if he travels the trail in the opposite direction. What is the length of the trail?

(A) 5 mile (B) 10 miles (C) 15 miles (D) 20 miles (E) 35 miles

Answer Key for Test Five

3-point problems	4-point problems	5-point problems
1. C	11. E	21. C
2. C	12. A	22. C
3. E	13. E	23. C
4. C	14. C	24. E
5. A	15. C	25. B
6. E	16. E	26. C
7. C	17. D	27. B
8. B	18. C	28. A
9. B	19. C	29. D
10. A	20. C	30. C

TEST NUMBER SIX

3-point problems

1. $104 \times 104 - 4 \times 4$ is:

   (A) 10000 **(B)** 10080 **(C)** 10400 **(D)** 10800 **(E)** 10036

2. Keira multiplied a number by 1000 instead of dividing it by 100. To get the correct answer, she must:

   (A) multiply her result by 10
   (B) divide her result by 10
   (C) multiply her result by 0.01
   (D) divide her result by 100000
   (E) divide her result by 0.001

3. The figure depicts a spring with a horizontal length of 20 units. If the drawing is to scale and segments that look equal are actually equal, what is the value of $4x$?

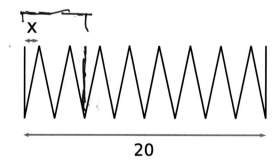

20

   (A) 2.5 **(B)** 5 **(C)** 10 **(D)** 16 **(E)** 40

4. Kangaroy bought 1 liter of orange juice. He drank 150 milliliters and gave 400 milliliters to Kangarob. Kangarob drank 2 deciliters and returned the rest to Kangaroy. How many centiliters of juice does Kangaroy have now?

(A) 55 (B) 60 (C) 65 (D) 550 (E) 650

5. Steve is filling a tub with water. In the first 2 minutes, he has filled one fifth of the tub. Then, while filling the rest, he took a break. He finished filling the tub 15 minutes after starting. How long was his break, in minutes?

(A) 1 (B) 2 (C) 3 (D) 4 (E) 5

6. If A, B, C, and D are different digits and the following operation is correct:

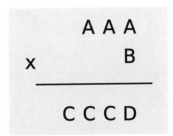

what is the digit D?

(A) 0 (B) 1 (C) 2 (D) 3 (E) 4

7. A non-leap year has more Sundays than Mondays. The next year starts on a:

(A) Monday (B) Saturday (C) Sunday (D) Tuesday (E) Thursday

8. Which number is greater:

   (A) $6.22 \times 10,000$ rounded to the nearest thousand
   (B) $0.062 \times 1,000,000$ rounded to the nearest ten thousand
   (C) $6,261,000 \times 0.01$ rounded to the nearest hundred
   (D) $0.58 \times 100,000$ rounded to the nearest ten thousand
   (E) $61.89 \times 1,000$ rounded to the nearest thousand

9. A chair is 8 feet away from a backpack and 14 feet away from a table, all on the same line. Maggie walks from the chair to the table and back, passing by the backpack each time. At least how many feet did Maggie walk to pass by the backpack 6 times?

   (A) 22 **(B)** 48 **(C)** 70 **(D)** 76 **(E)** 84

10. A cylinder rolls without sliding on ramps set in a zig-zag, like in the figure. Which choice represents the path traveled by the center of the top of the cylinder?

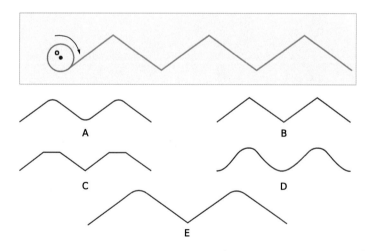

   (A) A **(B)** B **(C)** C **(D)** D **(E)** E

4-point problems

11. Four identical hexagons are used to make a frame for a rectangular mirror, like in the figure. What is the measure, in degrees of arc, of the angle marked with x?

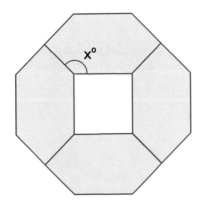

(A) 60° (B) 120° (C) 135°

(D) 150° (E) it depends on the thickness of the frame

12. At a florist's shop the sales of tulips and roses were summarized in a table. Some of the entries have been accidentally erased. Mandy calculates the missing values and enters them. How many more tulips and roses did they sell on Sunday than on Monday?

Table 7.1: Daily Sales of Tulips and Roses

	Sunday	Monday	Tuesday	Total
Tulips	250	150	120	520
Roses	240	160	200	600
Total	490	310		1120

(A) 150 (B) 160 (C) 170

(D) 180 (E) cannot be determined

13. Kangarob and Knagaroy found a pile of kiwi fruit. Kangaroy ate one third of them and pocketed two for a snack later on. Kangarob ate half of the rest and took three for snack. Then, three little joeys came along and found they could have exactly 5 fruit each before there were none left. At least how many kiwis were there in the pile initially?

(A) 27 (B) 36 (C) 57 (D) 72 (E) 76

14. 37 students are on the school's 8 tennis courts. Currently, there are either 2 people or 4 people playing on each of the courts. At least how many students are not playing?

(A) 1 (B) 3 (C) 5 (D) 7 (E) 9

15. In an isometric grid an ant may move one step at a time from a grid point to another. Initially, the ant is at point O.

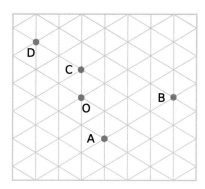

After exactly 6 moves, the ant cannot reach point:

(A) A (B) B (C) C (D) D (E) any of the choices can be reached

16. A racecar runs around a 3-mile racetrack in 1.2 minutes. Every 5 laps, it stops for 1.5 minutes. What is its average speed in miles per hour after completing 25 laps?

(A) 110 **(B)** 115 **(C)** 120 **(D)** 125 **(E)** 150

17. Kangaroy is allowed to hop only from a grid point to a neighboring grid point, following the grid lines of the figure.

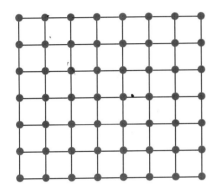

If each small square has a side length of one unit, what is the length of the shortest path Kangaroy can take in order to visit all the points of the grid?

(A) 42 **(B)** 45 **(C)** 55 **(D)** 56 **(E)** 97

18. Allison and Stella are writing random numbers on a whiteboard. At least how many numbers do they have to write to be sure that two of the numbers differ by a multiple of 11?

(A) 11 **(B)** 12 **(C)** 22 **(D)** 121 **(E)** an infinity

19. 30 hens eat 20 lbs. of feed in 15 days. How many hens will eat 36 lbs. of feed in 18 days?

(A) 3 (B) 18 (C) 28 (D) 42 (E) 45

20. Three cards are painted with a solid color as follows: one of them is painted red on both faces, another is painted green on one face and red on the other, and the third one is painted green on one face and blue on the other. Alina places them on the table in a row. How many different arrangements are there?

 (B) 8 (C) 12 (D) 15 (E) 24

5-point problems

21. On a straight road, Seville is equidistant from Deville and Beville, while Beville is equidistant from Seville and Aville. If the distance from Aville to Seville is 80 miles, what is the distance from Beville to Deville?

(A) 20 (B) 40 (C) 80 (D) 120 (E) 160

22. The line (l) can rotate around point P. At most how many intersections with the circles can it have?

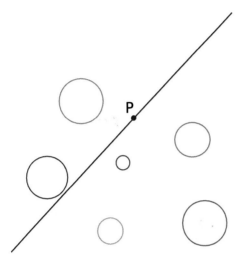

(A) 2 (B) 4 (C) 6 (D) 8 (E) 10

23. Find the product of the positive integer numbers a, b, c, d in the following correct expression:

$$\frac{13}{20} = \cfrac{1}{a + \cfrac{1}{b + \cfrac{1}{c + \cfrac{1}{d}}}}$$

(A) 2 (B) 7 (C) 6 (D) 13 (E) 20

24. An isosceles triangle $\triangle ABC$ has side lengths $50, 50$, and 60 units long, with $AB = AC$. What is the length of the segment BM which is perpendicular to AC?

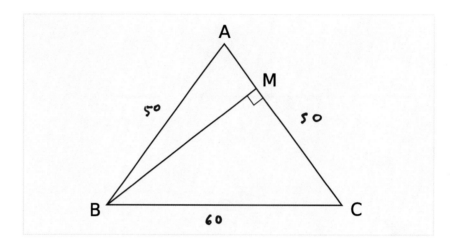

(A) 40 (B) 42 (C) 45 (D) 48 (E) 50

25. For the Math Kangaroo prize distribution at her school, Sandra purchased 15 objects for 860 dollars. Each prize consists of 5 objects, each costing either 100, or 70, or 50 dollars. There are three prizes, each of different value. What is the largest value the largest prize could have?

(A) 210 (B) 290 (C) 340 (D) 360 (E) 610

26. Five ants carried a pile of leaf cuttings to their colony. The first ant carried one sixth of the load, the second ant carried twice as much, the third ant carried one third of the remaining amount, the fourth ant carried half of the remaining, and the last ant finished the job by carrying away the rest. How many of the ants carried the same amount?

(A) 2 (B) 3 (C) 4 (D) 5 (E) each carried a different amount

27. In the following correct prime factorization, each digit has been replaced by a letter. Different digits are represented by different letters. The same letter represents the same digit.

   A B B A = C × A A × A D

The sum of the digits of the number *ABBA* is:

(A) 2 **(B)** 6 **(C)** 10 **(D)** 16 **(E)** 24

28. Hansel and Gretel went for a walk in the forest. They were afraid of losing their way and decided to leave some markings behind. They have a bagful of red pebbles and a bagful of blue pebbles. They leave pebbles on a line along the way so that, if they later come across the markings they will be able to tell which direction they were going in at the time they placed them. Which of the following patterns is the one they must have used?

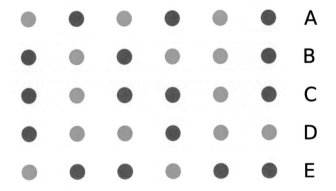

(A) A **(B)** B **(C)** C **(D)** D **(E)** E

29. A car leaves point M at the same time as a motorcycle leaves point N traveling toward each other. The car travels at a speed that is 20 mph higher than the speed of the motorcycle and they meet at time T. If the car would travel at the same speed as the motorcycle they would meet 45 minutes later than T. If the motorcycle would travel at the same speed as the car, they would meet 30 minutes earlier than T. If T is equal to 4:00 PM, what time did they both start?

   (A) 1:00 PM **(B)** 1:15 PM **(C)** 1:30 PM **(D)** 1:45 PM **(E)** 2:00 PM

30. A 3-digit number is called *valiant* if it has a prime factorization consisting of two 2-digit numbers so that one of them is the sum of the digits of the other. How many *valiant* numbers are there?

   (A) 0 **(B)** 1 **(C)** 2 **(D)** 3 **(E)** 4

Answer Key for Test Six

3-point problems	4-point problems	5-point problems
1. D	11. C	21. C
2. D	12. D	22. B
3. B	13. C	23. C
4. C	14. D	24. D
5. E	15. E	25. C
6. A	16. D	26. C
7. A	17. C	27. A
8. C	18. B	28. B
9. D	19. E	29. A
10. E	20. D	30. E

1. The easiest way to count is to match portions of the figure so as to get rectangular patches of each color. A possible arrangement is:

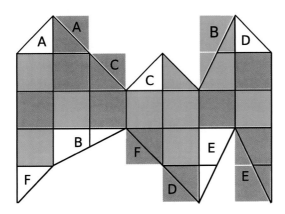

   There are 9.5 green squares and 11 orange squares. The total number of points is:

$$9.5 \times 2 + 11 = 19 + 11 = 30$$

   The correct answer is **(B)**.

2. Elaine has $0.25 \times 7 = 1.75$ dollars. Since $2.50 - 1.75 = 0.75$, Dan must have a total of 75 cents. The smallest amount of coins he must have is: 7 dimes and 1 nickel. The correct answer is **(D)**.

3. Notice that, in each row of the table, the numbers have a sum of 100. The number missing is 88 and its digit sum is 16. The correct answer is (**E**).

4. Each of the 5 friends could be friends with 2 people who already are among Sandra's friends. So the smallest number of people who come to the party is 5. Plus Sandra, there are at least 6 people at the party. Other assumptions lead to larger numbers of friends. The correct answer is (**B**).

5. The difference and the sum of two integers are either both even or both odd (have the same *parity*. Therefore, if the semi-difference is an integer then the difference is even and, consequently, the sum is also even. The correct answer is (**B**). If you ask why it is not always a multiple of 4, notice that it is relatively easy to find a counter-example: the numbers 9 and 5.

6. Notice that:

$$3 + 4 = 7$$
$$7 + 8 = 15$$
$$15 + 16 = 31$$

One possible way to continue the sequence is to add the next number: $31 + 32 = 63$. The correct answer is (**D**).

7. To make the multiple of 3 largest, we have to make the multiple of 5 also largest. The largest multiple of 5 that is smaller than 40 is 35. The largest multiple of 3 smaller than 35 is 33. The correct answer is (**A**).

8. Use the rule for divisibility by 3. At least one of the factors in the product must be a multiple of 3. Since $1 + 5 = 6$, the correct answer choice is (**A**).

9. Assume the number exceeds 18 by an amount x. Then, it exceeds 12 by $2x$. We have:

$$12 + 2x = 18 + x$$

and $x = 6$. The number is $12 + 12 = 24$.

10. All the fractions are equivalent to 2/3:

$$\frac{22}{33} = \frac{2 \times \cancel{11}}{3 \times \cancel{11}} = \frac{2}{3}$$

$$\frac{202}{303} = \frac{2 \times \cancel{101}}{3 \times \cancel{101}} = \frac{2}{3}$$

$$\frac{2002}{3003} = \frac{2 \times \cancel{1001}}{3 \times \cancel{1001}} = \frac{2}{3}$$

$$\frac{20002}{30003} = \frac{2 \times \cancel{10001}}{3 \times \cancel{10001}} = \frac{2}{3}$$

The correct answer is **(E)**.

11. Move 5 squares: the four blue squares into the green positions and the one red square into the orange position:

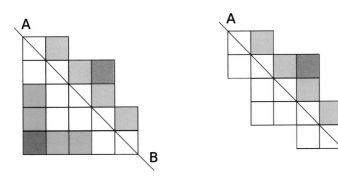

To prove that one has to move at least 5 squares, count the squares that are not on the line. There are 10 such squares. At least half of them will have to be moved. Therefore, a lower number is not possible, but it is still necessary to find an actual solution with 5 moved squares.

12. Since the orange field is immediately beside the center line, we must obtain a sum of 140 if we add it to its neighbor on the left. However, since the numbers must be different and in increasing order from left to right, the neighbor cannot be smaller than 4. the largest possible number in the orange field is $140 - 4 = 136$. The correct answer is **(D)**.

1	2	3	4	136	137	138	139

13. The second kangaroo is one fifth of the way away from the finish line. The third kangaroo is one third of the way from the finish line. They are separated by:
$$\frac{1}{3} - \frac{1}{5} = \frac{5-3}{15} = \frac{2}{15}$$
of the total distance. The correct answer is **(D)**.

14. Each pair of 2×5 is a factor of 10. Since there are 5 factors of 2 and 5 factors of 5, they can be paired to form 5 factors of 10. Therefore, the number is formed by a digit of 1 followed by 5 zeros. The correct answer is **(E)**.

15. Let R, G, Y be the numbers of apples in the red, green, and yellow bags, respectively. Then we have that:
$$R - 10 = G + 10 = Y$$
Therefore, $R = G + 20$ and $Y = G + 10$.

Also, we know that: $Y + 10$ is equal to twice $G - 10$. Replace Y by $G + 10$ and obtain that: $G + 10 + 10$ is twice $G - 10$:
$$G + 20 = G - 10 + G - 10$$
Therefore, $G = 40$. From here, we can easily infer that $R = 60$ and $Y = 50$. The correct answer is **(E)**.

16. The distance covered by Andy in 30 steps is equal to the distance covered by Tessa in 45 steps. The total distance that separated them at the start is, therefore, equal to $30 + 45 = 75$ of Tessa's steps. Each of them walks at a pace of 15 steps per minute. Therefore, it would take Tessa:

$$\frac{75}{15} = 5 \text{ minutes}$$

to walk the entire distance.

17. Re-organize and group the factors bearing in mind that we need numbers that are close. Notice that 2×3 is close to 5 and 19 is close to 23:

$$(2 \times 3 \times 19) \times (5 \times 23)$$

The two consecutive numbers are: $2 \times 3 \times 19 = 114$ and $5 \times 23 = 115$. Their sum is equal to 229. The correct answer is **(E)**.

18. The picture shows that 3 cups of water were consumed. If 3 cups represent 40% of the total capacity, then the kettle can hold $3 + 3 + 1.5 = 7.5$ cups of water. The correct answer is **(B)**.

19. There are multiple ways to achieve the goal but all of them involve canceling at least two flights, as it is necessary to eliminate all the loops. Since there are two loops, two connections must be broken. The correct answer is **(C)**. An example is:

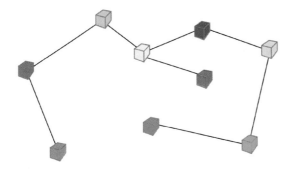

20. The statement of the problem implies that at least some of the 6th graders play multiple games.

If we assume that, for each 5th grader, only one different student in 6th grade is added, the rest having played before, we find that, at each step, it is possible to add only 2 players who have not played already: one in grade 5 and one in grade 6. Since we started with 2 students, we can add 2 more students 10 times, before we reach the total of 22. In this case, we would have 11 students in grade 5 and 11 students in grade 6. The last student in grade 5 would play 11 games. The correct answer is **(B)**.

21. Assume the unit fraction is $1/n$. Then, the operation of subtracting it from its denominator is:

$$n - \frac{1}{n} = \frac{n^2}{n} - \frac{1}{n} = \frac{n^2 - 1}{n} = \frac{(n-1)(n+1)}{n}$$

Since $\gcf(n, n+1) = 1$ and $\gcf(n-1, n) = 1$ the resulting fraction is always irreducible (in this context, 'always' means for any value of n). (Remember that two consecutive numbers do not have any non-trivial common factors.) The correct answer is **(A)**.

22. **Solution 1**
Since Jill has 2 cookies more than Anna and Jim has 3 cookies more than Anna, the following diagram represents the number of cookies each has:

Since there are 5 equal boxes and a leftover of 5 cookies, the total number of cookies is a multiple of 5. The correct answer is **(C)**.

Solution 2
Set the number of cookies Anna has to be x. Then, Jill has $x + 2$, Ben has $2x$, and Jim has $x + 3$. In total, they have:

$$x + x + 2 + 2x + x + 3 = 5x + 5$$

The total number is a multiple of 5, regardless of the value of x.

23. The expression is equivalent to:

$$\frac{5}{6} \div \frac{7}{11} = \frac{5}{6} \times \frac{11}{7}$$

Multiplication and division have the same priority in the order of operations. Therefore, they can be performed in any order. We just have to ensure that 5 and 11 are numbers we multiply by, while 7 and 6 are numbers we divide by. The only answer choice that does not conform to this is **(D)**.

24. Because the last digit of the product is the same as the last digit of both factors, A can only have the values $0, 1, 5$, or 6. 0 is ruled out because the leftmost digit cannot be zero. Moreover, if $A = 0$ then $B0 \times B0$ ends in 2 zeroes thus making B and C also zero.

However, since $500 \times 500 = 250000$ which is a 6-digit number, whereas the product $ABCBA$ is only a 5-digit number, the set of possible values for A consists of only one value: 1. Since $1 \times B = B$ we have that the second digit of the product B must be equal to $2B$. This means that $B = 0$ and:

$$101 \times 101 = 10201$$

is the unique solution. Therefore $A + B + C = 1 + 0 + 2 = 3$. The correct answer is **(C)**.

25. We can cut it into the following types of rectangular tiles:

1×1 (unit squares)

1×2

1×4

1×5

2×5

In total, 5 possible ways of cutting the rectangle into same size rectangles. Note that a 2×1 rectangle has the same size as a 1×2 rectangle - therefore, we should not count these as separate possibilities. The correct answer is (C).

26. Only two different ways:

- Alma writes to Leah's parents, Thea writes to Alma's parents, and Leah writes to Thea's parents;

- Alma writes to Thea's parents, Thea writes to Leah's parents, and Leah writes to Alma's parents;

The correct answer is (B). This problem is a simple introduction to counting *derangements*.

27. The eraser must be placed with the 5×3 face down and rotated around the side of length 3. In this way, we obtain a trace of length: $5 + 4 + 5 + 4 + 5 = 23$, which is also the longest possible. The correct answer is (B).

28. The fractions can be re-written to have the same denominator:

$$\frac{1}{8}, \frac{2}{8}, \frac{3}{8}, \frac{4}{8}, \frac{5}{8}, \frac{6}{8}$$

Notice that there are three possibilities for two of these fractions to have a sum of $\frac{7}{8}$:

$$\frac{1+6}{8} = \frac{1}{8} + \frac{6}{8}$$
$$\frac{2+5}{8} = \frac{2}{8} + \frac{5}{8}$$

$$\frac{3+4}{8} = \frac{3}{8} + \frac{4}{8}$$

Since the total number of ways that two fractions can be selected from the set is:

$$5 + 4 + 3 + 2 + 1 = 15$$

The number of pairs that do not have the specified sum is $15 - 3 = 12$. The correct answer is **(D)**.

29. The numbers are all multiples of 7:

$$
\begin{aligned}
a &= 7 \cdot x \\
b &= 7 \cdot y \\
c &= 7 \cdot z \\
d &= 7 \cdot w
\end{aligned}
$$

with x, y, z, and w numbers that have no factors in common. Therefore, the least common multiple must be:

$$\text{lcm}(a, b, c, d) = 7 \cdot x \cdot y \cdot z \cdot w$$

Dividing 210 by 7 we obtain 30 which has to be the product:

$$x \cdot y \cdot z \cdot w = 30$$

Since 30 has only 3 prime factors:

$$30 = 2 \cdot 3 \cdot 5$$

one of the numbers x, y, z, w must be equal to 1. The sum of the numbers is:

$$a + b + c + d = 7 + 14 + 21 + 35 = 77$$

The correct answer is **(E)**.

30. Since the area of the square is 49 square units, the length of the side of the square must be equal to 7 units. The rectangle formed has area $4 \times 4 \times 3 = 48$ square units if it does not have a hole,

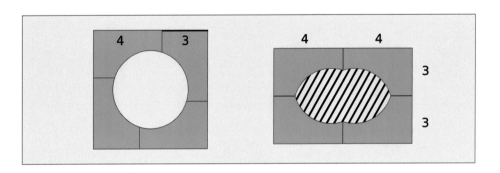

while the irregular shaped parts have a total area of:

$$49 - 12 = 37$$

Subtract the area covered by the irregular parts from the area of the rectangle to find the area of the shaded part:

$$48 - 37 = 11$$

HINTS AND SOLUTIONS FOR TEST TWO

1. Draw a straight line between the two houses. A straight segment is the shortest possible path. Count that 5 bridges will be needed. The correct answer is **(D)**.

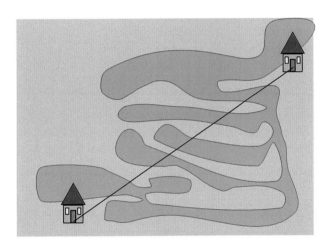

2. The members who tied for the first place were surely among those who were ahead of Jim. With 4 people ahead of Jim, Jim himself, and 3 people behind Jim, there are 8 members in the club. The correct answer is **(B)**.

3. 123 is larger than 98 by 25. The number that is larger than 12 by 25 is 37. The digit sum of 37 is $3 + 7 = 10$. The correct answer is **(B)**.

4. The correct answer is (**A**).

5. The correct answer is (**D**).

6. They can play 4 games from 2:35 to 4:35 and then another game between 4:35 and 5:10. The correct answer is (**D**).

7. During two minutes (one even and one odd) the bug moves 3 inches up from the previous point. For the first 12 minutes, the bug moves up $3 \times 6 = 18$ inches. During the next minute, it moves another 5 inches up, reaching the top of the window. The correct answer is (**D**).

8. To end in zero, the product must have at least one even factor and another factor that is a multiple of 5. The only product that does not have a factor of 5 is (**E**).

9. For the Readkins family to read a whole number of books, the number of days has to be a multiple of the numbers of days each of them takes to finish a book. Since $\text{lcm}(2, 4, 5) = 20$, the number of days has to be a multiple of 20. In 20 days, John reads 10 books, Alexa reads 5 books, and Tanya reads 4 books, for a total of $10 + 5 + 4 = 19$ books. Since $38 = 19 \times 2$, the number of days they take to read 38 books is equal to 40. The correct answer is (**D**).

10. If the digit sum of a number is divisible by 9, then the number is divisible by 9 (and by 3). If the digit sum is divisible by 3, and not divisible by 9, then the number is divisible by 3 and not by 9. Here is a table with the numbers, as well as their digit sums:

Number	69	96	312	405	522	339	1008	2001	777	333
Digit sum	15	15	6	**9**	**9**	15	**9**	3	21	**9**

There are 4 digit sums that are divisible by 9. The correct answer is (**B**).

11. The correct answer is (**A**), since it is not possible to see the ground level cube that may exist behind the gap.

12. Since the girls remain as a queue of three, there are six possible ways to permute them within the queue. Moreover, the queue may start in the first, second, or third positions. The two boys may also be permuted in two ways. The total number of choices is $6 \times 3 \times 2 = 36$. The correct answer is **D**.

13. The hexagon can be tesselated into 12 identical triangles. The triangle specified by the statement can be tesselated into 2 such smaller triangles.

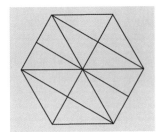

The area of the hexagon is larger than the area of the triangle by 500%. Use the definition of the percent increase, using the area of the triangle as the initial amount and the area of the hexagon as the final amount. Both areas are expressed in number of smaller triangles.

$$\frac{12 - 2}{2} \times 100\% = \frac{10}{2} \times 100\% = 500\%$$

The correct answer is (**D**).

14. The sequence starts at 5 and each term increases by 4. If we subtract 1 from 57 we should obtain a multiple of 4:

$$56 \div 4 = 14$$

This means 57 chips were taken out in the 14th round, counting the first round in addition to the 13. Divide 14 by 3 to find out which child took chips on the 14th round:

$$14 = 4 \times 3 + 2$$

Since the remainder is 2, it must have been Dan's turn. The correct answer is **(B)**.

15. Since the operator produces a ratio between the difference and the sum of two numbers, the ratio will remain the same if the numbers are multiplied by the same factor. For example:

$$\frac{5-2}{5+2} = \frac{10-4}{10+4}$$

With this observation in mind, we can see that in choice **(E)** the operator is not applied to numbers that are both the same multiple of 5 and 2.

16. **Solution 1** Since the first digit is either 1 or 2, the numbers are of the form $1a7$ or $2b7$, with a and b digits that have to be determined. For the numbers to have a digit sum divisible by 3 we have that a can be $1, 4,$ or 7, while b can be $0, 3, 6,$ or 9. However, $117, 267,$ and 297 are not in the desired range, leaving only 4 solutions.

Solution 2 It is easier to list the numbers that end in 7 and check if they are multiples of 3. The numbers in the specified interval that end in 7 are: $127, 137, 147, 157, 167, 177, 187, 197, 207, 217, 227, 237, 247$. Their digit sums are: $10, 11, 12, 13, 14, 15, 16, 17, 9, 10, 11, 12, 13$. Of these, only 4 are multiples of 3. The correct answer is **(B)**.

17. If x is the amount each of four students would contribute towards the same total as if ten students contribute y, then:

$$4x = 10y$$

and the percent change is:

$$\frac{y - x}{x} \times 100\% = \frac{0.4x - x}{x} \times 100\% = -60\%$$

The correct answer is **(C)**.

18. The number 4321 has two prime factors:

$$4321 = 29 \times 149$$

The correct answer is **(B)**.

19. At most 6 intersections. The correct answer is **(C)**.

20. Since $0.999\ldots = 1$, its double is equal to 2. The correct answer is **(E)**.

21. Since 64 is a multiple of 16, the closest multiple of 16 is 16 numbers away (either larger or smaller). The correct answer is **(D)**.

22. Since the angles of triangle $\triangle ABC$ have a sum of $180°$, the two acute interior angles of the small triangle have a combined measure of: $180° - 80° - 20° - 20° = 60°$. Its obtuse interior angle has a measure of $180° - 60° = 120°$ and the angle x has a measure of $360° - 120° = 240°$. The correct answer is (**E**).

23. When Tony replaced the green marbles the total number of marbles did not change. This number must be a multiple of 3 because at the end we have equal numbers of marbles of each color. There is only one multiple of 3 among the answer choices - 21. The correct answer is (**C**).

24. The possible values for the first number are elements of the set $4, 5, 6, 7$. The possible values for the second number are elements of the set $3, 4, 5$. The third number can have any value between the smallest and the largest element of the union set $3, 4, 5, 6, 7$. Therefore, there are 3 possible values for the third number. The correct answer is (**D**).

25. There are $51x$ chickens and $2x$ dogs. After a third of the chickens were sold, there were $51x - 17x = 34x$ chickens remaining, thus the ratio between the numbers of chickens and dogs was $34 : 2 = 17 : 1$. The ratio between the number of chickens' legs and dogs' legs was $17 \times 2 : 1 \times 4 = 17 : 2$. The correct answer is (**A**).

26. To find the reflection across point Q draw segments from at least two points of the original figure to Q, then extend each of them to double their length:

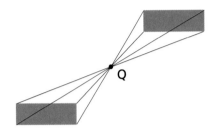

The correct answer is (**D**).

27. Group the birds into groups with one of each bird. Each group weighs: $5 + 8 + 11 + 19 = 43$ lbs. Find the least multiple of 43 that is greater than 465:

$$43 * 11 = 473$$

Find out which number must be subtracted from 473 to obtain 465:

$$473 - 465 = 8$$

The first bird that farmer Stan sold was a duck. The correct answer is (**B**).

28. The hours may have the values: 00, 11, and 22. The minutes may have the values: 00, 11, 22, 33, 44, and 55. In total $3 \times 6 = 18$ possible ways to pair them. The correct answer is (**E**).

29. The ones digit cannot be 0 because it is not the sum of any even digits. There is one possible number if the ones digit is 2: 202.

If the ones digit is 4, there are 2 possibilities: 404 and 224.

If the ones digit is 6, there are 3 possibilities: 606, 426, and 246.

If the ones digit is 8, there are 4 possiblities: 808, 628, 268, and 448.

In total, there are $1 + 2 + 3 + 4 = 10$ such numbers. The correct answer is **(A)**.

30. **Solution 1**

Notice that, in all the numbers certain identical digits are 3 place values apart, such as in: **1231653423**. This may indicate that the number may be a multiple of 1001. In turn, 1001 is a multiple of 13 since $1001 = 7 \times 11 \times 13$. Therefore, extending this observation further we notice that some of the digits are sums of digits that are 3 place values apart:

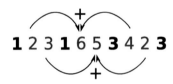

The number can be written as a sum of the two numbers:

$$12312300000 + 423423$$

Each of the numbers is divisible by 1001 since:

$$423423 = 400400 + 20020 + 3003$$

and

$$12312300000 = 10010000000 + 2002000000 + 300300000$$

If you apply this method to all the answer choices you find that all the numbers proposed are constructed in this same manner. Therefore, they all are multiples of 1001 (and, implicitly, of 13) except for answer choice (**E**) which is 12 more than a multiple of 13:

$$2512831333 = 25125100000 + 321321 + 12$$

Solution 2

A number of the form $abcdefg$ where a, b, c, d, e, f, and g are digits, can be written as:

$$\begin{aligned}
abcdefg &= abcd \times 1000 + efg \\
&= abcd \times 1001 - abcd + efg \\
&= 1001 \times abcd - 1001 \times a + a - bcd + efg
\end{aligned}$$

The number has the same remainder on division by 1001 as the alternating sum:

$$a - bcd + efg$$

1231653423 has the same remainder on division by 1001 as
$-1 + 231 - 653 + 423 = 654 - 654 = 0$

4815152342 has the same remainder on division by 1001 as
$-4 + 815 - 152 + 342 = 1157 - 156 = 1001$.
Etc.

HINTS AND SOLUTIONS FOR TEST THREE

1. From 8:15 PM to 6:15 AM there are 10 hours. From 6:15 to 6:35 AM there are 20 minutes. In total, the night lasted 10 hours and 20 minutes. The correct answer is **(B)**.

2. One hundred one hundred dollars are:

$$100 \times 100 = 10,000 \text{ dollars}$$

The correct answer is **(B)**.

3. Convert all the heights to the same unit. By converting to meters we obtain:

    Jim jumped 2.7 m

    Ben jumped 4 m

    Sam jumped 2.5 m

    Jon jumped 3 m

    Ali jumped 5 m

Ali made the highest jump. The correct answer is **(E)**.

4. Choice (A) is the product of an odd number with an even number, which is even. Choice (B) is the difference of two even numbers, which is even. Choice (C) is the product of an even and an odd number, which is even. Choice (D) is the difference between an odd number and an odd number, which is even. Choice (E) is the algebraic sum of five odd numbers, which is odd. The correct answer is **(E)**.

5. The original grid is 5×5 - there are 25 total small squares, of which 12 are of one color and 13 are of the other color. If we add a single column or a single row, the grid becomes $5 \times 6 = 30$ and has an equal number of squares of each color. Therefore, the first two operations should be counted as producing the correct result.

   If we add one row and then one more column, the grid becomes $6 \times 6 = 36$ which has an equal number of squares of each color - again, the desired result.

   If we add one row, then one column, then another row, the grid becomes $6 \times 7 = 42$ which has an equal number of squares of each color - again, the desired result.

   If we add one row, then one column, then another row, and then one more column the grid becomes $7 \times 7 = 49$ which cannot have an equal number of squares of each color.

   Therefore, a total of 4 operations produce the desired result. The correct answer is **(D)**.

6. One third of the cars is $57 \div 3 = 19$ cars. Each car has 4 tires. Tony has to install $19 \times 4 = 76$ winter tires. The correct answer is **(C)**.

7. Group the factors conveniently:

$$
\begin{aligned}
8 \times 0.125 &= 1 \\
2 \times 0.5 &= 1 \\
4 \times 0.25 &= 1
\end{aligned}
$$

The correct answer is **(C)**.

8. If the perimeter is equal to 8, then the sum of the longer side length and the shorter side length is equal to 4. The only different positive whole numbers that have a sum of 4 are 3 and 1. The area is equal to $3 \times 1 = 3$ square units. The correct answer is **(B)**.

9. If we write the three positive integers in increasing order $a < b < c$ we see that we obtain three fractions that are larger than 1: $b/a, c/a$ and c/b. The correct answer is **(D)**.

10. All operations have the result 20, except **(D)**:

$$\frac{9}{\frac{1}{4} + \frac{1}{5}} = \frac{9}{\frac{9}{20}} = 20$$

$$\frac{1}{\frac{1}{4} - \frac{1}{5}} = \frac{1}{\frac{1}{20}} = 20$$

$$4 \times 5 = 20$$

and

$$4 \times 4 + 4 = 20$$

11. Since the prime factorization of 1938 is

$$1938 = 2 \times 3 \times 17 \times 19$$

and the prime factorization of 1734 is:

$$1734 = 2 \times 3 \times 17 \times 17$$

the greatest common factor is:

$$\text{gcf}(1938, 1734) = 2 \times 3 \times 17 = 102$$

The correct answer is **(E)**.

12. Hannah has to make 4 creases in order to fold the vertices of the original square onto the center of the square. However, since the paper square is blank, Hannah does not know where the center is positioned. In order to find the position of the square, Hannah has to make two additional creases: either along the diagonals, or along the medians (lines that split the square into two identical rectangles.) Therefore, the order of operations for Hannah is:

First, determine the midpoints of the sides of the original square:

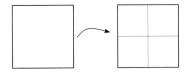

Now Hannah can fold the paper using the midpoints, to form a smaller square:

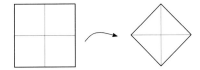

The correct answer is **(C)**.

13. Eliminate from the start answers (A), (B), and (E), which are clearly proper fractions, and focus on answers (C) and (D) which may be larger than 1. Calculate (C) to obtain:

$$\frac{1}{3} \div \frac{1}{7} = \frac{7}{3} = \frac{21}{9}$$

and (D) to obtain:

$$\frac{1}{\frac{1}{3} + \frac{1}{7}} = \frac{1}{\frac{10}{21}} = \frac{21}{10}$$

The correct answer is **(C)**.

14. If Kangarob owed Kangaroy 15 dollars, then Kanragoy's eggs cost $50 - 15 = 35$ dollars. Since Kangaroy purchased 7 dozens, then each dozen cost $35 \div 7 = 5$ dollars. Kangarob's eggs must have cost:

$$5 \times 12 = 60$$

dollars. Since he had to borrow 15 dollars from Kangaroy, then he must have had only:

$$60 - 15 = 45 \quad \text{dollars}$$

at the time of the purchase. The correct answer is **(D)**.

15. Since the entire figure is rotated, the triangle will continue to have one side that is parallel to a side of the square. The only figure in which there is no side of the triangle that is parallel to a side of the square is **(A)**.

16. The digit sums range from 0 to 18. There is one number with a digit sum of 0, as well as one number with a digit sum of 18 (99). There are two numbers with a digit sum of 1 (1 and 10) and two numbers with a digit sum of 17 (98 and 89). There are three numbers with a digit sum of 2 (2, 11 and 20) and three numbers with a digit sum of 16 (88, 97 and 79). The pattern continues, with each box containing an increasing number of numbers. There are two boxes with exactly four numbers inside: the box with digit sum 3 and the box with digit sum 15.

17. Since multiplying by 1 does not change a number, multiplying a number N by 10001 is the same as the sum $10000 \cdot N + N$. If Alex's number has 4 digits, it will satisfy the requirement. For example, take the 4-digit number 3456:

$$3456 \cdot 10000 + 3456 = 34560000 + 3456 = 34563456$$

The correct answer is **(C)**.

18. We must use 8 triangular faces to connect the two square bases:

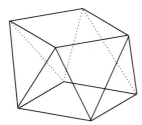

The correct answer is **(E)**. For your information, this type of solid is called an antiprism.

19. Robot A makes $5 \times 60 = 300$ zogs in one hour. Robot B is capable of making $6 \times 60 = 360$ zogs in one hour if it functions continuously. Because it had to pause, robot B produced 60 zogs less than it would have otherwise. Therefore, it has paused for $60 \div 6 = 10$ minutes. The correct answer is **(C)**.

20. Pretend that the train that turned the light on is not moving. Then, the other train moves towards it at a speed of $65 + 55 = 120$ mph. At this speed, it takes:

$$\frac{1.2}{120} \times 60 = 0.6 \text{ minutes}$$

for the moving train to meet the not moving one. After passing it, the light is left behind and is no longer visible.

Convert the minutes into seconds to find the answer:

$$0.6 \text{ minutes} = 0.6 \times 60 = 36 \text{ seconds}$$

The correct answer is **(C)**.

21. Each pair of white and grey triangles has triangles with the same area, because they have a common height and bases that are equal in length (they are both equal to the diagonal of the square):

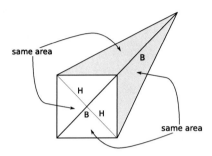

Therefore, the shaded area is equal to the area of the square. The correct answer is **(D)**.

22. If the days with rain are denoted by R, then the days without rain are $R + 20$. The total number of days is $2 \times R + 20$. The rainy days are 0.3 of the total number of days:

$$
\begin{aligned}
R &= 0.3(2 \times R + 20) \\
R &= 0.6 \times R + 6 \\
0.4 \times R &= 6 \\
R &= 60 \div 4 = 15 \\
R &= 15 \text{ days}
\end{aligned}
$$

The total duration of the study is $15 + 15 + 20 = 50$ days. The correct answer is **(A)**.

23. Since the prime factorization of 111 is $111 = 3 \times 37$, 111 and 7 are coprime. (Two numbers are coprime if their greatest common factor is 1.) The number she divided by 111 must be a multiple of both 111 and 7. The smallest such number is 7×111. The correct answer is **(C)**.

24. At the first operation, one fifth of the oil has been consumed and four fifths are left over. At the second operation, one fifth of four fifths (4/25) has been consumed and four fifths of four fifths are remaining (16/25). The third operation is similar. The diagram summarizes the process. The consumed fractions are in red and the remaining are in green:

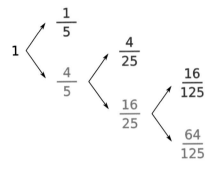

The fraction that has been consumed is:

$$\frac{1}{5} + \frac{4}{25} + \frac{16}{125} = \frac{25 + 20 + 16}{125} = \frac{61}{125}$$

Since the leftover oil is 61 gallons, the total amount of oil at the start of the process has been 125 gallons. Therefore, the remaining amount is exactly 64 gallons.

The correct answer is **(D)**.

25. **Solution 1**

For any triangle, the length of each side must be smaller than the sum of the lengths of the other two sides. Alissa can make the triangles with side lengths:

1, 2, 2

1, 3, 3 = 1 + 2

2, 3, 3 = 1 + 2

$$2, \ 2, \ 2 = 1 + 1$$
$$3, \ 2, \ 2$$
$$3, \ 3 = 1 + 2, \ 3 = 1 + 2$$
$$2, 3 = 1 + 2, 4 = 1 + 3$$
$$1, 4 = 3 + 1, 4 = 2 + 2$$

Esha can make 8 different triangles in total. The correct answer is **(C)**.

Solution 2

To enumerate all triangles write all ordered triplets $\{a, b, c\}$ with $a \geq b \geq c \geq 1$ and $a < b + c$. Discard those that canno the obtained by using the given stick lengths. These are the following 8:

$$\{4, 4, 1\}, \ \{4, 3, 2\}, \ \{3, 3, 3\}, \ \{3, 3, 2\}, \ \{3, 3, 1\}, \ \{3, 2, 2\}, \ \{2, 2, 2\}, \ \{2, 2, 1\}$$

26. After the first operation, the results of subsequent operations alternate between 20034 on even count operations and 20025 on odd count operations. Since 1000 is an even number of operations, the correct answer is **(B)**.

27. Jim bagged $\dfrac{1}{4}$ and Jack bagged $\dfrac{1}{8}$. Jared bagged:

$$\frac{1}{3} \times \frac{1}{8} = \frac{1}{24}$$

John bagged:

$$1 - \frac{1}{4} - \frac{1}{8} - \frac{1}{24} = \frac{7}{12}$$

This amount is 14 times larger than Jared's portion.

$$\frac{1}{24} \times 14 = \frac{7}{12}$$

The correct answer is **(B)**.

28. Chris removes chips according to the sequence:

$$3, 12, 21, 30, \ldots$$

and Emily removes chips according to the sequence:

$$9, 18, 27, 36, \ldots$$

By the time Chris has removed a total of:

$$3 + 12 + 21 + 30 = 66$$

chips, over a total of 4 turns at the game, Emily has only had 3 turns to go and has only removed:

$$9 + 18 + 27 = 54 \text{ chips}$$

The correct answer is **(A)**.

29. Dissect the figures, discard the darker areas, and re-assemble the lighter areas:

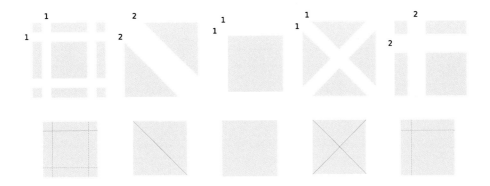

Each re-assembled figure is a square with side length equal to the side length of the original square minus 2 units. Therefore, all dark areas have the same area. The thin lines are guides only - they are not part of the re-assembled figure but they show which parts were assembled and how. The correct answer is **(D)**.

30. Since the statement guarantees that only one of the numbers is a perfect square, the simplest strategy is to look for the numbers that *cannot* be perfect squares. The last digit of a perfect square cannot be any of: 2, 3, 7, or 8. Therefore, only choice (**E**) can be a perfect square.

HINTS AND SOLUTIONS FOR TEST FOUR

1. Two fifths of the cake weigh three-fifths of a pound. Therefore, one fifth of the cake weighs:

$$\frac{1}{2}\frac{3}{5} = \frac{3}{10}$$

and the whole cake weighs:

$$\frac{3}{10} \times 5 = \frac{3}{2} = 1.5$$

The correct answer is **(B)**.

2. The following table summarizes the times at which they wake up:

K	5:25 AM
N	5:50 AM
G	6:05 AM
A	6:15 AM

Kangaroo R could wake up at 5:55 AM.
The correct answer choice is **(E)**.

3. The assemblies can have the heights:

$$2, 3, 4, 5, 6, 7, 8, 9, 10$$

for a total of 9 different heights. The correct answer is **(E)**.

4. Only the entries at the corners change both row and column. The correct answer is **(C)**.

5. It is not difficult to see that each pair of terms has a difference of 50. Therefore, the result is a multiple of 50. However, the difficulty consists in figuring out how many pairs of terms we have:

$$
\begin{array}{ll}
900 & -850 \\
800 & -750 \\
\cdots & \cdots \\
200 & -150
\end{array}
$$

We can count the pairs by counting how many numbers there are in the left column:

$$900, 800, \cdots, 200$$

This is the same number of numbers as in the sequence:

$$9, 8, \cdots, 2$$

Therefore, there are $9 - 2 + 1 = 8$ pairs and each adds 50 to the final answer. The result is $8 \times 50 = 400$. The correct answer is **(A)**.

6. After 4 hours and 45 minutes from the first photograph, it is midnight. The next day, 3 hours and 5 minutes have to elapse to complete the interval of 7 hours and 50 minutes between the two photographs. Therefore, the time of the second photograph is 3:05 the next day. The correct answer is **(E)**.

7. The Demon has to choose not only how many atoms to whack but also which is the more advantageous place to put them. In figure (A) it is best if the Demon moves 3 blue atoms in the right chamber and 4 yellow atoms in the left chamber. The total number of atoms moved is 7. By following the same reasoning in each case, we can summarize the results in a table:

Figure	Move to left	Move to right	Total moved
A	4 yellow	3 blue	7 atoms
B	3 yellow	3 blue	6 atoms
C	3 yellow	4 blue	7 atoms
D	4 yellow	2 blue	6 atoms
E	2 yellow	3 blue	5 atoms

The correct answer is (E).

8. If each different digit is repeated 3 times, then the sum of the digits is a multiple of 3, and so is the number. Only in choice (**D**) are there 4 digits of 1 and only 2 digits of 3, making the sum of the digits 16, which is not a multiple of 3.

9. If there are 10 juveniles, then there are 7 bucks and does combined, for a total of 17 animals. If there are 10 does, there is at least one buck, and the number of juveniles is $10+1+3 = 14$, for a total of $14+11 = 25$ animals. This is also true if we assume there are 10 bucks and one doe. The least number of deer is 17. The correct answer is (**A**).

10. If the area of a square is 121, its side is 11 and if the area of a square is 441, its side is 21. There are $21 - 11 + 1 = 11$ squares. The correct answer is (**B**).

11. In one box, Gina can fit at most $2 \times 2 \times 8 = 32$ blocks. This means that she will use 4 boxes, since $120 = 3 \times 32 + 24$. The correct answer is (**B**).

12. The statement translates into:

$$\frac{4}{100} \times x = \frac{1}{x}$$

which can be solved for x:

$$\frac{4}{100} = \frac{1}{x^2}$$
$$x^2 = \frac{100}{4}$$
$$x^2 = 25$$
$$x = \pm 5$$

Since x must be positive, it is equal to 5. All the statements are false except (**A**).

13. The diagram explains how the hiker who climbed to the top spent 3 hours traveling two-thirds of the total journey. This is exactly the length of path they have to travel to return from the campsite. The correct answer is **(D)**.

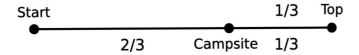

14. If:

$$3m + 5n = \frac{150}{100} \cdot 6m$$
$$30m + 50n = 90m$$
$$5n = 6m$$
$$100n = 120m$$

Then, $n = 120\%m$ and the correct answer is **(C)**.

15. One way of calculating the area of the triangle is:

$$A_{\triangle\ ABC} = \frac{BC \times AC}{2}$$

At the start $AC = 8$ inches and after 2 minutes, $AC = 6$. Since BC remains the same, the new area is:

$$\frac{6}{8} = \frac{3}{4}$$

of the initial area. The area of the triangle has decreased by 25%. The correct answer is **(E)**.

16. Since Carla and Jorge both told the total, only one of them is correct. Therefore, all the others speak the truth. Assume marbles are red, blue, and some other colors. Since there are 5 marbles of other colors, then out of the 13 marbles that are not blue only $13 - 5 = 8$ are red. Similarly, there are $11 - 5 = 6$ blue marbles. In total, there are $6 + 8 + 5 = 19$ marbles. Carla is wrong. The correct answer is **(B)**.

17. Avoid counting any segment twice. For example, color-code them before counting:

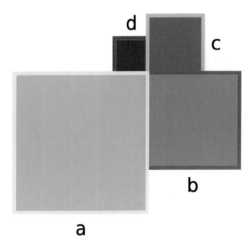

It becomes easy to see that the correct answer is **(E)**.

Alternatively, you can add the perimeters of all 4 squares and then subtract the edge lengths that were double-counted: the lengths of these segments add to $b + c + 2d$. Then, the perimeter of the figure is:

$$4(a + b + c + d) - 2(b + c + 2d) = 4a + 2b + 2c$$

18. Since:

$$\frac{2}{625} = \frac{2}{625} \times \frac{16}{16} = \frac{32}{1000} = 0.0032$$

while the other denominators cannot be transformed into powers of 10 since they factor as:

$$
\begin{aligned}
325 &= 5 \times 5 \times 13 \\
425 &= 5 \times 5 \times 17 \\
525 &= 3 \times 5 \times 5 \times 7
\end{aligned}
$$

The correct answer is **(E)**.

19. Add 2 to each number:

$$6, 12, 18, 24, \ldots, 204$$

and divide by 6:

$$1, 2, 3, 4, \ldots, 34$$

There are 34 numbers in the sequence. The correct answer is **(C)**.

20. Transform Tom's sequence:

$$
\begin{aligned}
98, 96, &\quad \cdots \quad 4, 2, 0 \\
49, 48, &\quad \cdots \quad 2, 1, 0
\end{aligned}
$$

and Jack's sequence:

$$
\begin{aligned}
0, 5, 10, 15, &\quad \cdots \quad 240, 245 \\
0, 1, 2, 3, &\quad \cdots \quad 48, 49
\end{aligned}
$$

When Tom says 46, the half of which is 23. This is the 27th term in the sequence since $49 - 23 = 26$. Therefore Jack says $26 \times 5 = 130$. The correct answer is **(C)**.

21. Compute the total number of coins remaining at each turn of the game:

Draw	Replace by	Change in gold coins	Change in silver coins	Change in total number
GG	none	−2	0	−2
SS	GG	2	−2	0
GS	GG	1	−1	0

Since the total is an odd number $(11 + 20 = 31)$ and changes at each turn by an even amount, it can never become zero or any even amount. Therefore, choices (B), (D), and (E) cannot happen. Since there is no turn at which the total increases, it is not possible for choice (C) to be true. It is possible, however, for **(A)** to happen.

22. Trace the segments AB and MN. Trace a line that is perpendicular at the midpoint of AB (pictured in red). Trace a line that is perpendicular at the midpoint of MN (pictured in green). The two lines split the plane into four sections. The section marked 'closer to A and to M' is the section of interest. There are 3 points inside it.
The correct answer is **(C)**.

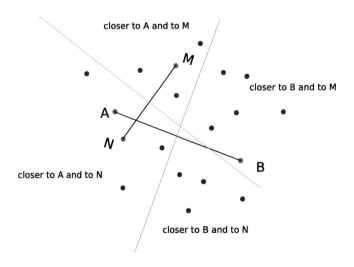

23. For each trapezoid, make a dissection consisting of a rectangle and two triangles. Than, paste the triangles together to form a larger triangle, like this:

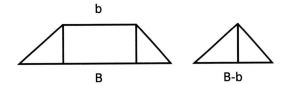

If the larger base is B and the smaller base is b, then the base of the resulting triangle is $B - b$. Now form all the triangles that correspond to the choices A-E:

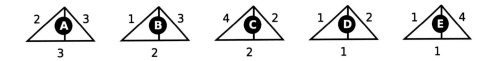

Only triangle **(A)** is possible. Triangle (B) is not possible because $1 + 2 = 3$, meaning the triangle would be only a segment; triangle (C) is not possible because $2 + 2 = 4$; triangle (D) is not possible because $1 + 1 = 2$; triangle (D) is not possible because $1 + 1 = 2 < 4$.

24. By the Pigeonhole principle, there must be at most 14 posters that are green and blue. Since the 14 posters represent 70% of the total number of posters, there are:
$$N = \frac{14 \times 100}{70} = 20$$
posters in total. Of these, 4 are blue, 6 are yellow, and 10 are green. The correct answer is **(A)**.

25. Assume the price of the merchandise to be P before any reductions are applied. If the 30% off reduction is applied, then Tanya has to pay only 70% of the original price - that is $0.7 \times P$.

If the \$20 off the entire purchase coupon is applied, Tanya pays $P - 20$. The two amounts differ by one dollar:

$$0.7 \times P + 1 = P - 20$$

Solve this linear equation for P:

$$21 = 0.3 \times P$$

to find the original price equals \$70. The price Tanya paid after the reduction was applied was:

$$70 \times 0.7 = \$49$$

The correct answer is (C).

26. Denote the 2-digit number AB by x. Then, $AC = x + 2$ and:

$$x \times (x + 2) = 100 \times C + x$$

which can be simplified as:

$$
\begin{aligned}
x^2 + x &= 100 \times C \\
x(x + 1) &= 2^2 \times 5^2 \times C
\end{aligned}
$$

Since x and $x + 1$ are consecutive, only one of them can be a multiple of $5^2 = 25$. Also, they must be of different parity, which means only one of them can be a multiple of 4. Since both are 2-digit numbers, we only have the following possibilities:

1. $x = 25, \quad x + 1 = 4 \times C$
2. $x = 4 \times C \quad x + 1 = 25$

Therefore, either $AB = 24, AC = 26$ or $AB = 25, AC = 27$. Since they must be consecutive even numbers, only the first solution is acceptable. We have:

$$24 \times 26 = 624$$

and $C = 6, B = 4, A = 2$. The correct answer is $(\mathbf{B})$.

27. There are 600 'even' operations and 600 'odd' operations. Therefore, the total rotation angle is:

$$600 \times 30° - 600 \times 90°$$

Factor a 600:

$$600 \times (30° - 90°) = -600 \times 60°$$

Since a complete rotation around the circle is either of:

$$360° \quad \text{or} \quad -360°$$

we notice that a number of complete rotations have been done:

$$\frac{600 \times 60}{360} = 100$$

After 100 rotations the arrow is back to its initial position. The correct answer is $(\mathbf{B})$.

28. There are only three possible ways to set up teams of two:

A, B	C, D
A, D	B, C

A, B	C, D
A, C	B, D

A, D	B, C
A, C	B, D

The correct answer is $(\mathbf{C})$.

29. Write $2015 = 2016 - 1$ and $2017 = 2016 + 1$ to find that:

$$2015 \times 2017 = (2016 - 1) \times (2016 + 1) = 2016^2 - 1$$

Therefore, the entire expression has the value 1. The correct answer is $(\mathbf{A})$.

30. Tony traveled the first mile at 15 miles per hour:

$$\frac{1}{4} \times 60 = 15$$

and the second mile at:

$$15 \times 1.4 = 21 \text{ mph}$$

The average speed is total distance (2 miles) divided by total time:

$$\frac{2}{\frac{1}{15} + \frac{1}{21}} = \frac{2}{\frac{7+5}{3 \cdot 5 \cdot 7}} = \frac{2 \cdot 3 \cdot 5 \cdot 7}{12} = \frac{35}{2} = 17.5$$

The correct answer is **(C)**.

HINTS AND SOLUTIONS FOR TEST FIVE

1. A day has 24 hours. There are 23 more hours in a day than in one hour. There are 23×60 more minutes in a day than in an hour. The correct answer is **(C)**.

2. There are few digits that differ by 7. The numbers are: $18, 81, 29, 92, 70$. The correct answer is **(C)**.

3. By connecting the midpoints of the neighboring sides we obtain a polygon with the same number of sides as the initial one. For example,

   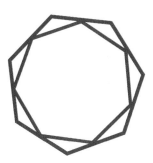

   The correct answer is **(E)**.

4. Since $7 \times 11 \times 13 = 1001$ (a fact that should generally be known), the answer is **(C)**.

5. The sequence is formed of two arithmetic sequences. One in which terms increase successively by 4 (common difference is 4):

$$3, 7, 11, 15, 19, \ldots$$

and one in which successive terms increase by 5:

$$4, 9, 14, 19, 24 \ldots$$

The next turn is for the first sequence and the term is $19 + 4 = 23$. Note that the terms do not continue in increasing order. The correct answer is **(A)**.

6. The rotations follow a pattern that repeats after 6 consecutive rotations. Divide 100 by 6:

$$100 = 16 \times 6 + 4$$

to find a remainder of 4. The figure below shows the positions of the assembly after the $1^{st}, 2^{nd}$, etc. rotations. The numbers that produce a remainder of 4 when divided by 6 are in the highlighted column.

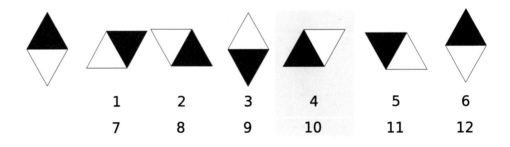

This corresponds to the position in choice **(E)**.

7. The numbers 1 and -1 are equal to their reciprocals:

$$\frac{1}{-1} = -1$$

$$\frac{1}{1} = 1$$

The number 0 does not have a reciprocal. The other numbers differ from their reciprocals:

$$\frac{1}{-10} = -0.1 \neq -10$$

$$\frac{1}{-0.1} = -10 \neq -0.1$$

$$\frac{1}{10} = 0.1 \neq 10$$

$$\frac{1}{0.1} = 10 \neq 0.1$$

Only the numbers 1 and -1 are equal to their own reciprocals. The correct answer is **(C)**.

8. The path is shortest if the truck avoids driving twice on any one street. For example, follow the red arrows to trace the blue contour and then the black arrows to complete the path. The length of the path is, in this case, $500 \times 3 + 400 \times 2 + 200 \times 2 = 1500 + 1200 = 2700$ feet. Since the truck drives each segment once, there is no shorter path possible. The correct answer is **(B)**.

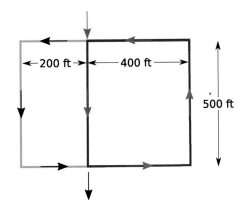

9. Since 20 oranges represent 40% of the capacity, then 5 oranges represent 10%, and 15 oranges represent 30%. The correct answer is **(B)**.

10. The correct answer is **(A)**, since all the other products are smaller than 280^2:

$$
\begin{aligned}
279 \times 281 &= (280 - 1)(280 + 1) = 280^2 - 1 \\
278 \times 282 &= (280 - 2)(280 + 2) = 280^2 - 2^2 \\
277 \times 283 &= (280 - 3)(280 + 3) = 280^2 - 3^2 \\
276 \times 284 &= (280 - 4)(280 + 4) = 280^2 - 4^2
\end{aligned}
$$

These identites should be visible at a glance and no calculation should be necessary.

11. Since for each of the triangles the white area is equal to half the area of the rectangle, it follows that the grey and dark areas combined are equivalent to half the area of the combined rectangles. Since the total area of both rectangles is:

$$\text{Width} \times \text{Height} = 12 \times 4 = 48$$

The grey and dark areas total to 24 square units. Subtract the grey area to find the dark area: $24 - 8 = 16$ square units. The correct answer is **(E)**.

12. We have that:

$$\frac{1}{7} < \frac{x}{6} < \frac{2}{3}$$

From the first inequality, we see that x has to fulfill:

$$7x > 6$$

which is true for any integer value x. From the second inequality, we obtain:

$$3x < 12$$

which means $x < 4$. There are 3 such fractions:

$$\frac{1}{6}, \quad \frac{2}{6} = \frac{1}{3}, \quad \frac{3}{6} = \frac{1}{2}$$

The correct answer is **(A)**.

13. Since the number is even, the product of its digits must be 2. The remaining digits must all be equal to 1. The number is:

$$11111111112$$

It is divisible by 2, since it is even; by 3 since the sum of its digits is $10 + 2 = 12$, by 4 since the last two digits form the number 12, and by 8 since 112 is a multiple of 8. It is not divisible by 16 since:

$$1112 = 16 \times 69 + 8$$

The correct answer is **(E)**.

14. Start by placing 3 chickens in each coop and leaving 8 chickens out. Now place each of the 8 chickens in a coop that already has 3 chickens in it. Now 8 of the coops have 4 chickens in them. The remaining coops have 3 chickens in them. Move these chickens 4 to a coop to leave one coop empty. This could only be done if there were 4 coops with 3 chickens. We obtain 3 coops with 4 chickens in each and one empty coop. Therefore, the total number of coops is $8 + 4 = 12$. Andy can place 4 chickens in each of 8 coops and 3 chickens in each of the remaining 4 coops. The correct answer is **(C)**.

15. The acute angles are:

$$10°, 20°, 30°, 40°, 50°, 60°$$

with an average of:

$$\frac{10 + 20 + 30 + 40 + 50 + 60}{6} = \frac{60 \times 70}{12} = 35°$$

The correct answer is **(C)**.

16. Since $1000^{1001} = 1000^{1000} \times 1000$, you can factor:

$$1000^{1000} times 1000 - 1000^{1000} = 1000^{1000}(1000 - 1) = 999 \times 1000^{1000}$$

Since 1000 has only 2 and 5 as prime factors, factor 999 to find out if there are larger factors:

$$999 = 3 \times 3 \times 3 \times 37$$

Therefore, the largest prime factor of the product is 37. The correct answer is **(E)**.

17. When a number and the sum of its digits are both divided by 3, the remainders are the same. Therefore, if we:

   - subtract the sum of the digits from the number we obtain a multiple of 3.
   - add to the number $2, 5, 8, \ldots$ times the sum of its digits, we obtain a multiple of 3.
   - add to the sum of the digits a multiple of $2, 5, 8, \ldots$ times the number, we obtain a multiple of 3.

Only the answer **(D)** does not necessarily match any of these rules. For example, the number 13 with sum of digits 4: $13 + 4 = 17$ which is not divisible by 3.

18. Tile NW is unchanged after 4 minutes. Tile NE is unchanged since $180 \times 2 = 360$. Tile SW also remains unchanged, since it rotates a full circle each time. Tile SE is unchanged since $\dfrac{3}{4} \times 4 = 3$ - therefore, it makes 3 complete rotations.

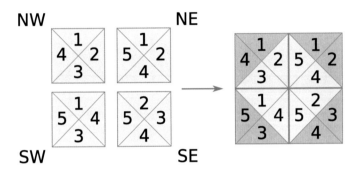

The sum of the numbers in the shaded area is: $4+1+1+2+3+4+3+5 = 8 + 10 + 5 = 23$. The correct answer is **(C)**.

19. **Solution 1**

Assume there are x colors in total. Then, the number of groups of 2 different colors is:

$$_xC_2 = \frac{x!}{2!(x-2)!} = \frac{x(x-1)}{2}$$

We must have:

$$\frac{x(x-1)}{2} = \geq 10$$
$$x(x-1) = \geq 20$$

x must be at least 5, since $4 \times 5 = 20$. The correct answer is **(C)**.

Solution 2 (without combinations and factorials)

Assign as few colors as possible. With 3 colors - say A, B,C, - we can satisfy the conditions for at most three children:

$$AB, AC, BC$$

Add one more color D:

$$AB, AC, BC, AD, BD, CD$$

to reach a maximum number of 6 different combinations.

Finally, by adding one more color E:

$$AB, AC, BC, AD, BD, CD, AE, BE, CE, DE$$

we are able to find 10 different combinations.

20. Use the fact that, if a radius is perpendicular onto a chord, then it bisects the chord. Therefore, the segment BM is congruent to the segment BC - both have a length of 3 units. On the other hand, the other side of the shaded rectangle has a length of $4 - 3 = 1$ unit, by the segment addition postulate.

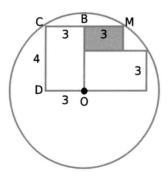

The area of the shaded rectangle is $3 \times 1 = 3$ square units. The correct answer is **(C)**.

21. Assume 34 can be written as a sum of 6 different even numbers. Then, 17 could be written as a sum of 6 different numbers. However, the smallest sum that 6 different numbers can have is:

$$1 + 2 + 3 + 4 + 5 + 6 = \frac{6 \times 7}{2} = 21$$

Therefore, since 34 is even, at least two of the numbers in the sum must be odd. Indeed, we can easily find an example:

$$34 = 5 + 9 + 2 + 8 + 6 + 4$$

The correct answer is **(C)**.

22. Denote the speed of the newer harvester with X and the speed of the older harvester with Y. The newer harvester worked for 15 hours and the older one worked for 8 hours. Therefore, the total amount of work done is:
$$15X + 8Y$$

and it is equal to the work done in the second scenario:

$$14X + 9Y$$

Therefore:

$$\begin{aligned} 15X + 8Y &= 14X + 9Y \\ X &= Y \end{aligned}$$

the speeds of the two harvesters are equal. The correct answer is **(C)**.

23. Coprime numbers are numbers whose only common divisor is 1. If the numbers are not coprime, then they must have a common divisor different from one. Call this divisor δ. If δ divides Anna's number, then it also divides its double. If we double Anna's number though and we subtract it from Tim's we obtain 5. Since any number that divides two numbers also divides their difference, $\delta = 5$. The initial number must be one less than a multiple of 5. For example, this could happen if the initial number were 9. Then Anna would have 10 and Tim would have $18 + 7 = 25$, and $\gcd(10, 25) = 5$. The correct answer is **(C)**.

24. We start with 16 yellow and 4 orange balls. For the yellow balls to be 60% of the total, their ratio to total must be:

$$\frac{3}{5} = \frac{12}{20} = \frac{15}{25} = \frac{18}{30} = \frac{21}{35} = \cdots$$

since the total is never smaller than 20. If the total is 25, then Jamie has added 5 balls, of which 4 are orange and only 1 is yellow. Therefore, the number of yellow balls is 17, not 15.

If the total is 30, Jamie has added 10 balls, of which 7 are orange and 3 are yellow. The number of yellow balls is $16 + 3 = 19$, not 18.

If the total is 35, Jamie has added 15 balls, of which 10 are orange and 5 are yellow. The number of yellow balls is $16 + 5 = 21$.

25. The longest chain is $(2, 0), (0, 0), (0, 1), (1, 1)$. The correct answer is **(B)**.

26. The segments obtained have 6 different possible lengths:

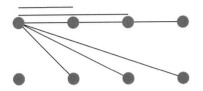

The correct answer is (C).

27. The product of two numbers is generally larger than the sum, unless we multiply by zero or by one. Therefore, the *florid* 2-digit numbers are:

$$
\begin{aligned}
&= 10, 11, 12, 13, \cdots, 19 \\
&= 20, 21 \\
&= 30, 31 \\
&= \cdots \\
&= 90, 91
\end{aligned}
$$

In total, $10 + 16 = 26$ numbers. The correct answer is (B).

28. Anna steps on tiles:
$$1, 5, 9, 13, 17, 21, \ldots$$

and Stella steps on tiles:

$$4, 10, 16, 22, 28, 34, 40, \ldots$$

The first sequence consists only of odd numbers. The second sequence consists only of even numbers. Since no odd numbers are even and conversely, there is no tile that they both step on. The correct answer is (A).

29. The largest number of empty planks happens when there are two birds on one third of the planks and one bird on:

$$\frac{1}{2} - \frac{1}{3} = \frac{1}{6}$$

of the planks. If the number of planks is P then the number of birds is:

$$\frac{P}{6} + 2 \times \frac{P}{3} = \frac{5}{6} \times P$$

If there are 30 birds, then there must be 36 planks. Of these, there is at least one bird on each of 18 planks and 18 planks can remain free, since the additional birds can form pairs with the others. The correct answer is (D).

30. Denote the long way up by $2l$ and the shorter way up l. The time, in hours, it takes Jeremy to climb up the long way is:

$$\frac{2l}{3}$$

and the time, in hours, it takes him to climb down the shorter slope is:

$$\frac{l}{5}$$

His total time one way is:

$$\frac{2l}{3} + \frac{l}{5}$$

The time, in hours, it takes him to travel in the opposite direction is:

$$\frac{l}{3} + \frac{2l}{5}$$

and this time is known to be shorter by 40 minutes. The 40 minutes must be converted to hours, to match the other times we determined:

$$
\begin{aligned}
\frac{l}{3} + \frac{2l}{5} + \frac{40}{60} &= \frac{2l}{3} + \frac{l}{5} \\
\frac{l}{5} + \frac{4}{6} &= \frac{l}{3} \\
\frac{2}{3} &= \frac{l}{3} - \frac{l}{5} \\
\frac{2}{3} &= \frac{2l}{15} \\
15 \times 2 &= 2l \times 3 \\
5 &= l
\end{aligned}
$$

Since the entire trail is equal to $2l + 2 = 3l$, the answer is $5 \times 3 = 15$. The correct answer is **(C)**.

HINTS AND SOLUTIONS FOR TEST SIX

1. Since $(104 + 4)(104 - 4) = 108 \times 100$, the correct answer is **(D)**.

2. Keira must divide her result by 1000 to obtain the original number, then she must divide this number by 100. Overall, she must divide her result by 100000. The correct answer is **(D)**.

3. The entire length of the spring can be matched to $16x$. Therefore:

$$\frac{20}{16} \times 4 = 5$$

The correct answer is **(B)**.

4. Convert all quantities to the same unit. Most convenient is to use the smallest unit mentioned, i.e. the mililiter. Kangaroy bought 1000 milliliters of orange juice. He drank 150 milliliters and gave 400 milliliters to Kangarob. At the end of these operations, Kangaroy was left with $1000 - 150 - 400 = 1000 - 550 = 450$ milliliters.

   Kangarob drank 200 milliliters and returned 200 milliliters to Kangaroy. Now Kangaroy has $450 + 200 = 650$ milliliters. Convert to 65 centiliters to find the answer.

5. If Steve took 2 minutes to fill one fifth of the tub, he will take 10 minutes to fill it completely without taking a break. Therefore, his break lasted 5 minutes. The correct answer is **(E)**.

6. Since the number AAA is a multiple of 111 and $CCC0$ is also a multiple of 111, D can only have the value 0:

$$A \times 111 \times B = C \times 111 \times 10 + D$$
$$111 \times (A \times B - 10 \times C) = D$$

Since D is a single digit, it can only have the value 0 while $A \times B = 10 \times C$). Since C is a single digit and:

$$A \times B = 2 \times 5 \times C$$

either $A = 5$ and B is an even digit or $B = 5$ and A is an even digit. The correct answer is (**A**).

7. Since,
$$365 = 7 \times 52 + 1$$

there are 52 whole weeks in a year, plus one day. This means there are 52 of each day of the week, except for one week day of which there are 53 occurences. If this is a Sunday, then it must be the first as well as the last day of the year. The next year starts on a Monday. The correct answer is (**A**).

8. The numbers are:

$$6.22 \times 10,000 = 62,200 \rightarrow 62,000$$
$$0.062 \times 1,000,000 = 62,000 \rightarrow 60,000$$
$$6,261,000 \times 0,01 = 62,610 \rightarrow 62,600$$
$$0.58 \times 100,000 = 58,000 \rightarrow 60,000$$
$$61.89 \times 1,000 = 61,890 \rightarrow 62,000$$

The correct answer is (**C**).

9. Every odd pass is from the chair to the table and every even pass is from the table to the chair. After passing the backpack 5 times, Maggie is at the table. From the table, she has to walk 6 feet to reach the backpack. The total distance walked up to this event is:

$$14 \times 5 + 6 = 76$$

The correct answer is **(D)**.

10. The correct answer is **(E)**.

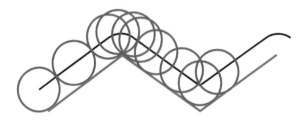

The center of the cylinder moves on a line parallel to the slide until the cylinder reaches the top and starts to pivot around the tip of the slide. At the bottom of the slide, the center reverses to climbing suddenly, as the cylinder reaches the bottom of the trough. Make the experiment using a vitamin bottle and some cardboard slides.

11. As the hexagons are identical, subtract 90° from a whole circle: $360° - 90° = 270°$ and divide by 2:

$$270° \div 2 = 135°$$

The correct answer is **(C)**.

12. The total number of tulips sold is: $1120 - 600 = 520$. Subtract the number of tulips sold on Sunday and Tuesday to find the number of tulips sold on Monday: $520 - 250 - 120 = 520 - 370 = 150$.

The number of tulips and roses sold on Monday is $150 + 160 = 310$.

The number of roses sold on Monday is: $600 - 200 - 160 = 400 - 160 = 240$. The total for Sunday is $250 + 240 = 490$.

There were $490 - 310 = 180$ more roses and tulips sold on Sunday than on Monday. The correct answer is **(D)**.

13. Use backsolving. The joeys ate:

$$3 \times 5 = 15$$

units. Add back the 3 units taken by Kangarob for a snack:

$$15 + 3 = 18$$

This was half of the leftover. The leftover was:

$$18 \times 2 = 36$$

Add back the 2 units taken by Kangaroy for a snack:

$$36 + 2 = 38$$

This was two thirds of the total, with one third of the total equal to: $38 \div 2 = 19$ and the total:

$$19 \times 3 = 57$$

The correct answer is **(C)**.

14. The least possible number of people not involved in playing is achieved when we have the largest possible number of courts occupied by 4 people each. Since there is at least one court with 2 people, we may assume there are 4 players on each of 7 courts. The total number of players would be:

$$7 \times 4 + 2 = 30$$

with 7 people not playing. The correct answer is **(D)**.

15. If the shortest path between two vertices is of length 6 or less then one can build a path of length exactly 6 by using the transformation:

which increases the length by one unit. For example, for the path from O to C, which is one unit long, one can do the transformations:

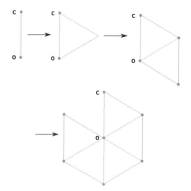

to increase this length to 6. Since all the lengths of the shortest paths from O to A, B, C, and D, are all less than 6 units long, all paths can be transformed into paths with length exactly equal to 6 units. The correct answer is **(E)**.

16. The racecar spends $1.2 \times 25 = 30$ minutes completing 25 laps and $1.5 \times 4 = 6$ minutes in cumulated stops, for a total time of 36 minutes. During this time, the racecar has traveled $3 \times 25 = 75$ miles. Its average speed is obtained dividing the total distance by the total time:

$$\text{Avg}_{\text{speed}} = \frac{75}{36} \times 60 = 125 \text{ mph}$$

The correct answer is **(D)**.

17. There are several paths of shortest length. For any of them, Kangaroy has to hop once for every point (vertex) of the grid except the first one. One example is:

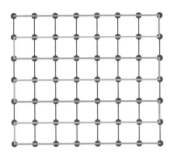

The length of any shortest path is:

$$8 \times 7 - 1 = 55$$

The correct answer is **(C)**.

18. For this, the two numbers must have the same remainder when divided by 11. Since there are 11 remainders possible, according to the Pigeonhole Principle, there must be at least 12 numbers on the whiteboard to ensure that two of them differ by a multiple of 11. The correct answer is **(B)**.

19. 30 hens eat $\dfrac{4}{3}$ lbs. of feed in one day. One hen eats $\dfrac{4}{90}$ lbs. in one day. In 18 days, one hen eats $\dfrac{4}{5}$ lbs. of feed. 36 lbs. of feed will be eaten by:

$$36 \div \frac{4}{5} = 36 \times \frac{5}{4} = 9 \times 5 = 45 \text{ hens.}$$

The correct answer is **(E)**.

20. The following arrangements are possible:

- (R,R,G) which can be arranged in 3 ways: (R,R,G)(R,G,R)(G,R,R).

- (R,R,B) which can be arranged in 3 ways: (R,R,B)(R,B,R)(B,R,R).

- (R,G,G) which can be arranged in 3 ways: (G,G,R)(G,R,G)(R,G,G).

- (R,G,B) which can be arranged in 6 ways.

The total number of arrangements is: $3 + 3 + 3 + 6 = 15$. The correct answer is (**D**).

21. Since $BC = CD$ and $AB = BC$, all three distances are equal: $AB = BC = CD$. Since $AC = 80$ we have that $BD = 80$ as well. The correct answer is (**C**).

22. The largest number of intersections is 4. Experiment by drawing the line in different positions:

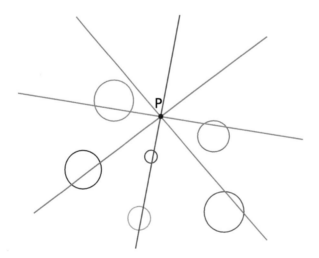

The correct answer is (**B**).

23. Write the fraction $\dfrac{13}{20}$ as a continued fraction:

$$\dfrac{1}{\frac{20}{13}} = \dfrac{1}{1 + \frac{7}{13}}$$

$$= \dfrac{1}{1 + \frac{1}{\frac{13}{7}}}$$

$$= \dfrac{1}{1 + \frac{1}{1 + \frac{6}{7}}}$$

$$= \dfrac{1}{1 + \frac{1}{1 + \frac{1}{\frac{7}{6}}}}$$

$$= \dfrac{1}{1 + \frac{1}{1 + \frac{1}{1 + \frac{1}{6}}}}$$

Identify the numbers: $a = 1, b = 1, c = 1, d = 6$. The product is $1 \times 1 \times 11 \times 6 = 6$. The correct answer is (C).

24. Since the triangle is isosceles, it has a line of symmetry that is perpendicular onto the base BC, bisecting it:

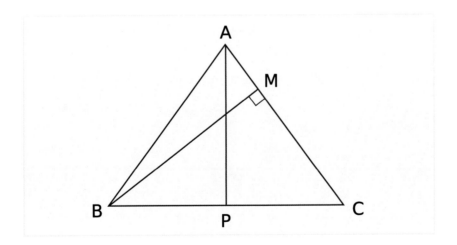

Therefore, the segment AP has a length of 40 units. Notice that now the triangle $\triangle APC$ is a right angle triangle with side lengths forming a

Pythagorean triple: $30, 40, 50$. Since $AP = 40$, the area of the triangle is:

$$A_{\triangle\ ABC} = \frac{60 \times 40}{2} = 1200$$

as well as:

$$A_{\triangle\ ABC} = \frac{AC \times BM}{2} = \frac{50 \times BM}{2}$$

We find BM:

$$
\begin{aligned}
25 \times BM &= 1200 \\
BM &= 1200 \div 25 \\
BM &= 48
\end{aligned}
$$

The correct answer is **(D)**.

25. The smallest possible prize value is $50 \times 5 = 250$ dollars. If we try to make the smallest prize exactly equal to 250, the values of the two larger prizes would equal $860 - 250 = 610$. Since $70 \times 3 = 210$, we can try to use three ojects values at 70 dollars each among the first two prizes. The remaining $15 - 8 = 7$ objects must be valued at $610 - 210 = 400$ dollars. We see that it is possible to use the smallest possible prize value for the third prize with the following distribution of objects:

$$
\begin{aligned}
100 + 70 + 70 + 50 + 50 &= 340 \\
70 + 50 + 50 + 50 + 50 &= 270 \\
50 + 50 + 50 + 50 + 50 &= 250
\end{aligned}
$$

The prizes must be different! The largest possible prize value is 340 dollars. The correct answer is **(C)**.

26. The first carried one sixth, the second carried two sixths. The remaining amount is exactly one half of the total. The third ant carried one third of one half, which is exactly one sixth. The remaining amount is two sixths, which the last two ants split exactly, so that each carried one sixth. Of the five ants, four carried one sixth each and only one carried a different amount. The correct answer is **(C)**.

27. Since the equality represents a prime factorization, the numbers C, AA, and AD must be prime. 11 is the only prime repdigit with 2 digits, so $A = 1$. Since AD is also prime, it can only be $13, 17,$ or 19. Since $A = 1$, the product of the digits C and D must end with the digit 1. The only such different digits are: $3 \times 7 = 21$. Therefore, AD is either 13 or 17 and C must be 7 or 3, respectively. Since $ABBA$ is a 4-digit number, and $A = 1$, only $C = 7$ has a chance of making the product sufficiently large. Therefore:

$$7 \times 11 \times 13 = 1001$$

and the sum of the digits of 1001 is 2. The correct answer is **(A)**.

28. To be able to tell which direction they were coming from, the pattern must be different when read backwards. First, copy each pattern several times in a row. Then, reverse them. Observe whether they read the same when reversed.

Of the patterns shown, only Red Blue Red Blue Blue Red is different if read backwards, since the red is a separator and the numbers that are separated are 1 and 2. One can make a rule that the larger number shows the 'to' direction and the smaller shows the 'from', or conversely.

All other patterns are the same when read backwards. The correct answer is **(B)**.

29. Assume the speed of the motorcycle is m, then the speed of the car is $m + 20$. If they meet after t hours, the total distance from M to N is:

$$D = mt + (m + 20)t = 2mt + 20t$$

If the car would travel at a speed of m, then they would meet after $t + \frac{3}{4}$ hours. The distance D is:

$$D = 2(m)(t + \frac{3}{4})$$

If the motorcycle would travel at a speed of $m + 20$, then they would meet after $t - \frac{1}{2}$ hours. The distance D is:

$$D = 2(m + 20)(t - \frac{1}{2})$$

Then, we have:

$$2mt + 20t = 2(m)(t + \frac{3}{4})$$

$$2mt + 20t = 2(m + 20)(t - \frac{1}{2})$$

Cleaning up:

$$2mt + 20t = 2mt + \frac{3}{2}m$$

$$2mt + 20t = 2mt + 40t - m - 20$$

Next:

$$40t = 3m$$

$$20t = m + 20$$

This means:

$$3m = 2m + 40$$

and, therefore, $m = 40$ mph. The car travels at 60 mph and $t = \dfrac{3m}{40} = 3$ hrs.

The correct answer is **(A)**.

30. Both factors are 2-digit prime numbers - therefore, they are odd. Moreover, since the sum of 2 digits cannot exceed 18, one of the numbers is $11, 13$, or 17. Call this number p. The other number must have an odd last digit and an even first digit, so that their sum is odd.

If $p = 11$, then the other number can be: $29, 47, 65, 83$. Of these, 65 is not prime. We have:

$$11 \times 29 = 319$$
$$11 \times 47 = 517$$
$$11 \times 83 = 913$$

If $p = 13$, then the other number can be: $49, 67, 85$. Of these, only 67 is prime:

$$13 \times 67 = 871$$

If $p = 17$, then the other number can be only 89, but the product would be a 4-digit number.

There are 4 *valiant* numbers. The correct answer is (**E**).

Math Challenges for Gifted Students

Practice Tests in Math Kangaroo Style for Students in Grades $1-2$
Practice Tests in Math Kangaroo Style for Students in Grades $3-4$
Practice Tests in Math Kangaroo Style for Students in Grades $5-6$

Competitive Mathematics Series for Gifted Students

Practice Counting (ages 7 to 9)
Practice Logic and Observation (ages 7 to 9)
Practice Arithmetic (ages 7 to 9)
Practice Operations (ages 7 to 9)

Practice Word Problems (ages 9 to 11)
Practice Combinatorics (ages 9 to 11)
Practice Arithmetic(ages 9 to 11)
Practice Operations (ages 9 to 11)

Practice Word Problems (ages 11 to 13)
Practice Combinatorics and Probability (ages 11 to 13)
Practice Arithmetic and Number Theory (ages 11 to 13)
Practice Algebra and Operations (ages 11 to 13)
Practice Geometry (ages 11 to 13)

Self-help:

Parents' Guide to Competitive Mathematics

Coming Soon:

Weekly Math Club Materials for Students in Grades 1 and 2
Weekly Math Club Materials for Students in Grades 3 and 4

Practice Word Problems (ages 12 to 15)
Practice Algebra and Operations (ages 12 to 15)
Practice Geometry (ages 12 to 15)
Practice Number Theory (ages 12 to 15)
Practice Combinatorics and Probability (ages 12 to 15)

Made in the USA
Las Vegas, NV
20 January 2024

84624874R10090